QUEEN EUPHORIA

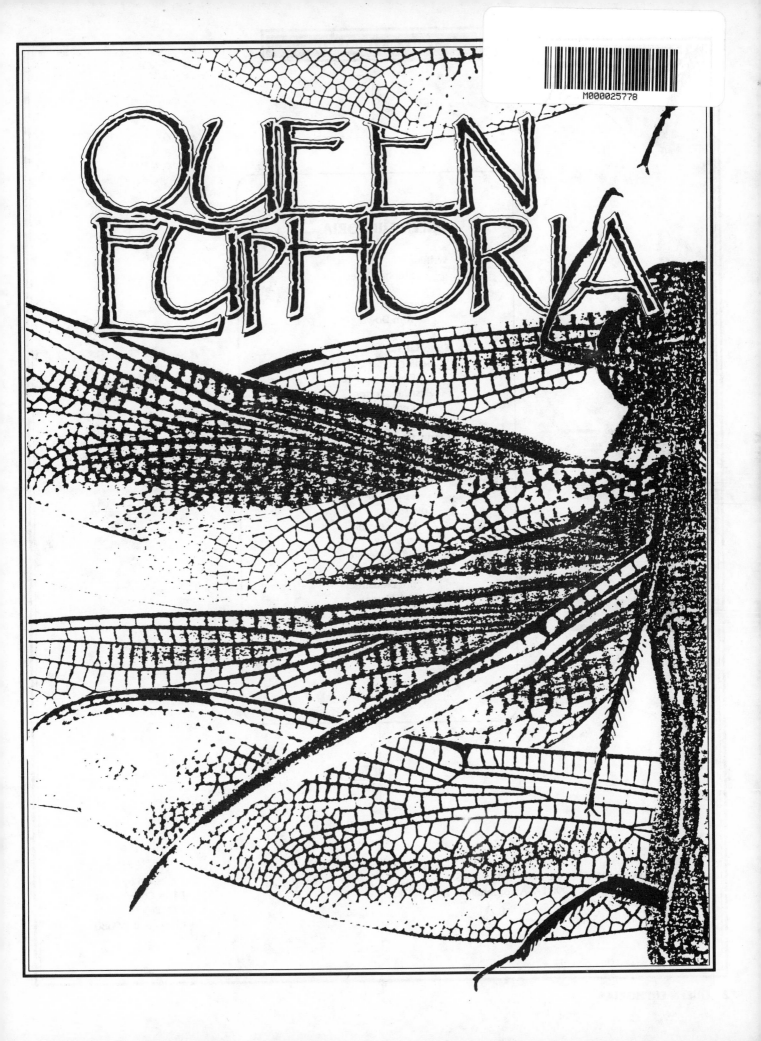

QUEEN EUPHORIA

Writing
Stephan Wieck

Development
Tom Dowd

Editorial Staff
Senior Editor
Donna Ippolito
Assistant Editor
Kent Stolt

Production Staff
Art Director
Dana Knutson
Production Manager
Sam Lewis
Cover Art
John Zeleznik
Cover Design
Jeff Laubenstein
Illustration
Tim Bradstreet
Rick Harris
Joel Biske
Layout
Tara Gallagher

Published by
FASA Corporation
P.O. Box 6930
Chicago, IL 60680

TABLE OF CONTENTS

ANT LION: A Prologue

Here in this silent, alien world, far from the streets of Seattle, the trap was shutting around him. He had felt it ever since the start of the run, and now his mounting sense of danger seemed to have reached some critical point.

He sensed that, here in this damned jungle, he was going to die.

The calm of the jungle made the foreboding the more unbearable. Dorin could live with the idea of death by a sudden bullet because the touch-and-go business of the streets might turn against him, but in this infinitely patient jungle, the wait was agonizing. What was he doing here? The city was where he belonged, the streets, whose staccato rhythm matched that of his own body, spirit, and magic.

He stared down through the cockpit window at the ocean of jungle vegetation rolling as far as the eye could see. As his hired pilot skimmed the Federated Boeing tilt-wing just over that ocean of green, the hypnotic, dull buzz of the rotors sent his mind drifting back over the past several days.

It had all begun when Solomon Daniels, his Fixer in Seattle had contacted him. Daniels, who supplied Dorin's talismonger shop with fetishes and other magical supplies, had discovered the source of his own supplier's fetishes. The corp with whom Daniels did business could not have realized the value of such information or they would have guarded it more closely. With knowledge of sources, a customer could bypass his middleman, even if that middleman were a large corp. What Solomon learned was that two primitive communities in the South American jungles were the source of the fetishes. The local shamans made and sold them to the supply corp for almost nothing. Hey, see a buck, make a buck, Dorin thought. Such was the will of Coyote.

So it was that Solomon hired Dorin to make a run into the jungle to buy up as many fetishes as possible at the low wholesale price. Dorin had jumped at the chance. He liked the thrill of a run, and swiping the fetishes out from under the noses of the corp buyers appealed to his spirit. Though the first premonition of doom had stirred even then, Dorin ignored it as mere jitters. But on every step of the run, the feeling grew more intense until it was almost tangible. He felt like an ant caught in an ant lion's trap, sliding inexorably down through the sand into the jaws of death.

He tried to shake it off, thinking he must stop taking everything so seriously. Just then, the pilot said something in what could have been either Spanish or Portuguese, and pointed out across the jungle. It was their destination, the little village of thatched roofs enclosed like an island in the ocean of green.

They'd already made quite a haul at the first village, and Dorin was expecting to totally pack the rotorcraft's cargo with plunder from this one. But he also hoped there'd be no repeat of his strange reception at the first village.

The pilot had landed the F-B in a clearing near the first village, and Dorin had hopped out to greet the villagers even before the rotors stopped turning. He had been smooth, rehearsed, and prepared with a smattering of the tribe's dialect. When the shamans appeared, they received him with supreme politeness mixed with caution. But when they thought he wasn't looking, Dorin caught them giving him odd stares, especially one shriveled husk of a man whose beady eyes never left Dorin. The deal went off without a hitch, the shamans not even attempting to negotiate. At first, he thought it was because they didn't know he would have paid more, then he suddenly realized that they were afraid of him. They wanted him to leave, and quickly.

While the villagers loaded up the plane, Dorin couldn't help but look back at the old man with the beady eyes. Wrapped in a faded blanket, the weathered shaman continued to gaze intently at Dorin. But the look was one of sympathy, perhaps pity. Then the man's eyes filled and a single tear ran down one creased cheek, driving Dorin's sense of spiritual doom deep into his soul.

Again, he tried to shake it off. The old man had no right to pity him, he thought angrily. Why were they treating him like this? Nothing had happened and nothing would. He wanted to go up to the old shaman and scream, "Stop looking at me like I'm a ghost! And don't pity me. I don't want your pity and I don't need it!" But by then, the villagers had finished loading the cargo, and Dorin didn't want to risk an outburst that no one would understand anyway.

A cry from his pilot brought him back to the present. What happened next seemed to go in stop motion as though the light from the sky were a dance floor strobe light. What the pilot saw was a sleek silver and blue jet fighter that knifed through the clouds like a bolt of lightning, then whistled down. A missile dropped from under the fighter's wing, and for one long moment, hung in the sky. Then reality accelerated as the missile fired and blazed toward the rotorcraft. Dorin's pilot jerked frantically at the craft's controls, but the missile struck.

The concussion threw Dorin forward against his safety belt and slammed his head into the cockpit window, dazing him. The rotorcraft was completely out of control, spinning in a mad vertigo. He tried to concentrate on a spell, but his head throbbed from the window impact. He could hear the rotorcraft smashing through vegetation in its descent, and he tried to brace for impact. When it came, the pilot's side of the plane slammed into the ground, buckling the metal. The breath was torn from Dorin's lungs on impact.

The aircraft slid to a halt, carving a long furrow in the jungle floor. The rotorcraft just lay there on its side, with Dorin buckled in his seat and suspended above the ground. As he gasped painfully for breath, he caught traces of the smell of smoke. Glancing down, Dorin saw the pilot lost in a twisted mangle of sheet metal and flesh.

Smoke billowed around him as an electrical fire crackled

from behind in the remains of the aircraft, but the door above Dorin had buckled on impact and sealed. Concentrating his will, he felt a surge of magic course into his hand, knitting the flesh into tough leather and then into a hard enamel. With a punch, his hardened hand smashed through the cockpit window, shattering the glass in a wave on concentric rings. He hammered on the window several more times until the entire frame of glass popped out, then he dropped the spell. His head already ached with needles of pain from the effort of sustaining magic. Choking on the smoke now pouring through the shattered window, Dorin unbuckled his safety belt and climbed through the window.

He slid down the nose of the aircraft and staggered several meters away, where he slumped down against a tree. Panting heavily as his muscles quivered with remaining adrenalin, he touched his aching head and felt his hair wet with something warm and sticky. When Dorin took his hand away, his fingertips were smeared with crimson. He was certain he must have some kind of concussion.

Through his dazed state, Dorin tried to evaluate the situation. The jet that had shot him down must certainly belong to the corp he'd been sent to undercut, and they would certainly come looking for the wreckage of his rotorcraft. They must have discovered Dorin's visit to the first village and mobilized to catch him at the second. The situation looked bleak. They couldn't be far off, and he had no food and only his urban survival skills in the middle of a jungle. He had a probable concussion, too, with no spell to cure it.

But Thomas Dorin laughed. Hadn't he cheated death? A presentiment of spiritual doom had screamed death from the start of this run, and he had cheated it. For once, his Coyote spirit was wrong. This, ironically, gave him strength. He was a survivor. He would continue to face the challenges before him and survive. He considered conjuring a spirit to conceal the wreckage, but it would take too much out of him to call up a spirit powerful enough to conceal the crash site. Instead, he stood up and prepared to set off east toward the ocean. In a brief flash, the sense of foreboding returned stronger than ever, but Dorin dismissed it fearlessly and began to walk.

Delirium soon replaced any other thoughts as physical exertion made his head injury worse. One day passing into the next, he could barely distinguish between hallucination and reality. Stumbling through the heavy vegetation, it was as though he moved through a surreal world of dreams. He had lost any desire for food or water and any conscious sense of direction, yet he felt drawn toward some goal. And all the while, his Coyote spirit warned him of death. Now he was sure it was his totem, not just some sixth sense. At times, he would follow phantom coyotes through the jungle only to end up walking in circles, or worse yet, continue to plod on toward his nameless goal.

After the eighth day, Dorin's physical and spiritual resources gave out and he collapsed. He was passing through an area overgrown with vines, but it felt as though his body were touching something made from stone. Before he could wonder about that, he slipped or was pushed into the astral plane. His astral form, so different from Dorin's ripped muscular physique, dressed in the flashy clothes he favored, was naked and emaciated. And yet, he seemed to perceive everything so clearly and consciously. The stone monument before him had a

clear astral image that radiated strong magic. The monument was an unmarked pyramid four meters high and just as wide.

A phantom coyote identical to those he had chased through the jungle appeared alongside him. As Dorin watched, the coyote's fur began to move, almost to writhe. Peering closer at the astral form, he saw that the coyote was swarming with large warrior ants, each one the size of one of Dorin's thumbs, and with square heads and thick mandibles. As the coyote looked sadly at him, for an instant Dorin saw its face replaced by that of the old shaman with the beady eyes and tears of pity. Then the phantom uttered a long and lonesome howl. As the mournful sound died away, the coyote collapsed. Immediately, the ants devoured its body, and the phantom corpse soon disappeared under the writhing mass of insects. All the while, Dorin experienced the scene as though through time-elapsed photography. When the body was gone, Dorin felt empty inside and knew that he had not escaped. The trap had shut around him.

And then the ants began to pour over him, burrowing into his skin and rooting out great chunks of his astral flesh. But he was like a spectator, watching it all happen, his consciousness removed from the destruction of his astral body. The ants carried the bits and pieces of his astral form up into the pyramid, with several carrying each rib and a swarm carrying his bare skull. As the procession reached the top of the monument, it began to disappear down through a hole into the pyramid. At that point, Dorin's clarity of vision seemed to dim. He wasn't sure exactly, but perhaps it was that the ants were rebuilding his astral body in the murky interior of the pyramid.

Then he understood. Power. They offered him power. Real power, not just the freedom of that stupid Coyote. The possibilities danced before him, dark sparks glowing with energy. A figure danced before him. Young and beautiful, she was everything he had ever wanted. With this new power, he would have her. She would be his, she would be his Queen.

Thomas Dorin threw back his head and laughed as the sparks danced around him.

She would be his Queen.

INTRODUCTION

Queen Euphoria is a roleplaying adventure set in the world of **Shadowrun.** The year is 2050. Advances in technology are astonishing, with Humans able to blend with computers and travel through that netherworld of data known as the Matrix. Even more astonishing is the return of Magic. Elves, Dragons, Dwarfs, Orks, and Trolls have assumed their true forms, while megacorporations (rather than superpowers) rule much of the world. Moving among it all like whispers in the night are the shadowrunners. No one admits their existence, but no one else can do their secret work.

This story takes place in the streets and shadows of the Tacoma, Puyallup, and Redmond Districts of the Seattle metroplex, now an urban sprawl encompassing some 1600 square miles on the eastern shore of Puget Sound. Yet even this vast megaplex is but an enclave set amid even larger states ruled by Native American nations and other sovereign states of Metahumans and Awakened Beings.

GAMEMASTERING NOTES

Queen Euphoria uses a decision-tree format, meaning that the players' team could arrive at the same encounter via various different routes, depending on choices that they make during roleplay. They could also just as easily miss a planned encounter altogether. To run the adventure, the gamemaster needs a thorough familiarity with the contents of this booklet as well as a working familiarity with the basic **Shadowrun** rules. The contents of this booklet are for the gamemaster's eyes only, except for certain items earmarked as handouts for the players. Everything needed to roleplay **Queen Euphoria** is included here.

Queen Euphoria is designed for a party of four to eight player characters. The group should contain a variety of talent, including at least one magician and one decker. Note also that combat skills will also be *very* important to a successful run. The gamemaster may also use pre-generated character types from the **Shadowrun** basic rules and from **Sprawl Sites**, FASA's **Shadowrun** sourcebook.

This adventure combines several approaches. Some encounters are thoroughly planned out and described in detail. Others merely set the scene and remain open-ended. Hints for gamemastering the various situations are included with the individual sections that make up **The Adventure.**

MAKING SUCCESS TESTS

During the course of the adventure, the players will make a number of Unresisted Success Tests using a skill and a given Target Number. These Unresisted Success Tests are indicated by the name of the appropriate skill and the Target Number. For example, a Stealth (4) Test refers to an Unresisted Stealth Success Test with a Target Number 4. Sometimes it is necessary to make die rolls against a Success Table that includes different information for different levels of success.

HOW TO USE THIS BOOK

Aside from the basic **Shadowrun** rules, this book includes everything needed to play this adventure. The gamemaster should read through the entire module before beginning the game. Some important plot developments will not become apparent until well into the adventure, but the gamemaster will have to lay the groundwork much earlier on. He can only do that by being familiar with the storyline.

The gamemaster should also examine the maps, plans, and diagrams found throughout **The Adventure**. Where appropriate, the map is coded with letters and numbers to link a section to an actual encounter description.

Though this book tries to cover all the likely—and even unlikely—things that can happen during the adventure, it is impossible to foresee everything. The gamemaster may find that sometimes it is a good idea to just let the unexpected lead where it will.

The **Plot Synopsis** is a summary of both the story background and the course the adventure is intended to follow.

The Adventure begins with the section entitled **Wake Up Call**. Following that are a number of short sections describing each of the encounters that the players will face or are likely to face in the course of roleplaying **Queen Euphoria**.

Most of the encounters begin with a text entitled **Tell It To Them Straight**. This is intended to be read, verbatim, to the shadowrunners. It describes where they are and what is happening to them as though they were there. Any special instructions to the gamemaster are printed in boldface type and signaled by the words "**Gamemaster's Notes.**"

Next comes the information entitled **Behind The Scenes**. This is the real story, for only the gamemaster knows what is really going on at any given moment in an adventure. If there is a map needed to play this encounter, it is included in this section. Non-player character stats needed to roleplay the section are usually included here, too.

Finally, each section includes hints entitled **Debugging**. These notes often include suggestions for getting the story back on track if things go too far wrong. For example, most gamemasters will not want the characters to get too discouraged or kill off too easily. The gamemaster is, of course, always free to ignore these hints and let the chips fall where they may.

Legwork contains the information the player characters can obtain though their contacts or through the public data nets.

The **Cast Of Characters** includes pre-generated player and non-player character descriptions and stats.

Picking Up The Pieces includes tips on Awarding Karma and contains newsnet items for handout to the players, depending on the outcome of the adventure.

There are also several **Player Handouts**, including a news item relating to the run, with a version appropriate to either a successful or unsuccessful run.

PLOT SYNOPSIS

There are things loose in the world that should not be. Thomas Dorin, also known as Craft, has brought back a terrible secret from the depths of the South American jungle: Insect Spirits.

Under the influence of the still-unsummoned Queen Ant Spirit, Craft has begun the formation of a Hive in preparation for her coming. In doing so, he has discovered a strange phenomena: when the secretion extruded by the Workers of this particular Hive is mixed with traditional food thickeners and additives, it creates a tasty, almost addictive junk food, or stuffer. To raise money to support himself and the Hive, Craft has offered Vincent Burroughs of Strice Foods a deal. Craft will provide Burroughs with quantities of the food substance in exchange for nuyen and secrecy. Desperate for success within the corp, Burroughs agreed, without knowing the true source of this "nectar of the gods."

Not even the executives of Strice are aware of the secret deal between Craft and Burroughs. As long as Burroughs can produce Amber Gel, the name given to the stuffer product, they don't care how he does it. The Bottom Line.

To promote their new product, Strice hires megasimsense star Euphoria, normally a recluse, to promote her favorite stuffer. If the series of appearances are successful, they will thrust Amber Gel into the international spotlight. Currently, the product is wildly successful, but is only being marketed in Seattle.

Having learned of the planned promotions, Strice Foods rival, Ludivenko, wishes to prevent her from showing up at any of the appearances scheduled over a single weekend. Ludivenko hopes that this will make Strice break their contract with Euphoria as well as creating adverse publicity for Amber Gel.

Elliot Whitecastle, a local Fixer, is recruited to locate a team.

As arranged, the shadowrun team kidnaps Euphoria and takes her into hiding. Meanwhile, Strice Foods decides to run the promotions without their star, desperately hoping to save the situation. Riots break out when Euphoria doesn't show up at one of the scheduled appearances. MegaMedia, the simsense production giant, is also enraged because Euphoria is their biggest star. Losing her would be a severe blow.

Acting quickly, Strice hires another shadowrunner, an African shaman named Pride, to find Euphoria. Using ritual magic and a strand of Euphoria's hair from her penthouse, Pride tracks the star down and leads an attack against the kidnappers. By sheer luck, the shadowrunners defeat Pride and spirit Euphoria off to another hideout. There she remains until the following Monday. With all her scheduled appearances past, the runners can release her.

Strice Foods and MegaMedia are unable to agree on compensation for the missed Euphoria appearances, though both know it was arranged by outsiders. They agree instead to fight it out in court for the next decade.

Ludivenko, seeing an opportunity, approaches MegaMedia and makes a similar deal for a series of similar public appearances by Euphoria to endorse their new Amber Gel copycat product, Blue Bacosoy.

Learning of the Ludivenko-MegaMedia deal, Burroughs fears that negative publicity surrounding the fiasco of the Strice promotions, combined with competition from Ludivenko, could severely damage Amber Gel. He is already having problems because production has almost ceased, while the demand keeps growing. Not realizing that Craft has an intense, perhaps psychotic, fascination for Euphoria, Burroughs instructs him to "take care of Euphoria." The near-mad insect shaman sees this as the opportunity to finally make Euphoria "his Queen."

Using Soldiers and Workers from the Hive, Craft raids Euphoria's penthouse and grabs her during a home-studio simsense recording session. Unknown to him, her equipment continues to make a simsense record all during the kidnapping. He takes her back to the Hive, begins the Queen Spirit summoning, and places Euphoria in a cocoon to begin her metamorphosis.

With Euphoria's second disappearance, MegaMedia is more furious than ever. Ludivenko reveals to them its involvement in the first Euphoria kidnapping and identifies the Fixer and runners involved. MegaMedia puts Robert Carrone, Euphoria's former manager and now a MegaMedia vice president, in charge of finding and bringing her back. Carrone, believing the runners might be involved again or at least have some information, hires them to find her.

First, he takes them to Euphoria's penthouse, where the kidnapping took place. The scene is one of carnage. All Euphoria's bodyguards have been slaughtered in a manner so gruesome that reason suggests nothing Human could have done it. As they search the apartment, the runners find the simsense recording Euphoria was making at the time of her abduction. It documents, in vivid detail, her experience as *something* broke in, killed her guards, and seized her. Also visible on the recording are two men. One wears a T-shirt with a "Garraty's Bar and Grill" logo and the other, whose look is crazed, mentions the name "Burroughs". Carrone suspects this "Burroughs" may be one and the same with Vincent Burroughs of Strice Foods.

There are a few leads to follow up. The first takes the runners to Garraty's Bar and Grill, where they learn of the disappearance of waiter Van Willis and his later sighting in the Barrens near a shop called "Magic Crafts". The second clue leads them to Burroughs.

Having conned their way into Burroughs' office, the runners learn some of the history of Amber Gel. If they can protect Burroughs from a sudden attack by a Soldier Ant Spirit, they may also learn more about the man named Craft.

Another option is the penetration of Strice Foods computer system, where the runners can learn a little about Amber Gel production and Craft.

All roads lead to the Amber Gel production facility hidden in the Puyallup Barrens. Deep in its belly, the runners will find Craft and the beginnings of the Ant Spirit Hive. What else will they find there? And will they live to tell about it?

TELL IT TO THEM STRAIGHT

Read the following to a character with an appropriate personality:

You wake up to the sound of your wristphone chirping away in the darkness. Your head pounds and your mouth feels like something between cotton and sandpaper. You have dim memories of a bartender with metal teeth who called himself The Earl and served you neon sake late into the night. Your throat feels raw, but you congratulate yourself for at least having enough sense to rent a coffin where you could pass out. Next time you paint the town, you'll practice some restraint. Hah.

You give a hoarse whisper and the lights come on. Then you thumb the receive switch. The tiny vidscreen flashes up, showing a man in an expensive suit. His black hair is slicked back and he has green cybereyes.

"Greetings, chummer," he says. "I've got a job for you and your pals."

See Behind The Scenes for more information on the vidphone conversation. Once all the basics have been covered, read the following:

"Remember, my friend, Pier 36 at eleven o'clock. Don't be late and be sure everyone is there. Mr. Johnson won't risk an appearance in an unsecured area. You know how the biz works."

The vidscreen fades to a prismatic point of light in the center of the screen and then dissolves to black. You lie down again to ease your throbbing head. A speaker on the side of the coffin squawks, and a metallic voice reminds you that check-out time is near. It's going to be a long day, but maybe, just maybe, you can recover some of the nuyen you blew last night.

BEHIND THE SCENES

The man on the phone is Ellery Whitecastle, a Fixer hired by the Ludivenko Corporation to assemble a shadowrun team to kidnap…er…detain the simsense star Euphoria. Whitecastle is to set up a meet between some runners and an executive Mr. Johnson from Ludivenko. He knows of the player characters through his own street sources, and has decided to offer them the run. If the team has gone through the **Shadowrun** adventure **Mercurial**, Whitecastle will have contacted them because of their prior experience with a big-name star.

Whitecastle's vidphone call is brief, but complete. His Fixer fee depends on the characters showing up to meet Mr. Johnson, so he will repeat important points to be sure the character understands everything. Whitecastle informs the character, whom he knows only by his or her street name, to assemble some associates (the other player characters) and meet with a

Mr. Johnson at Pier 36 on the Tacoma docks at eleven o'clock that evening. He reveals no details of the run nor can he say for whom Mr. Johnson works because Whitecastle does not know (though he suspects it is Ludivenko).

Whitecastle explains that the run should be profitable. "Based on the fee I am being paid to contact your team, your compensation should be considerable." Once the player character agrees, read the final part of **Tell It to Them Straight**.

Whitecastle himself is a moderately successful Fixer. (Use the **Fixer** Contact, page 167, **SR** rules.) He does well enough to dress in style and live in comfort. He performs almost all his business over the phone, rarely appearing in person. If the characters want to find out more about Whitecastle before their meeting on the pier, go to the **Legwork** section, p. 56.

DEBUGGING

All that can go wrong here is that the player character does not agree to the meet or does not contact the rest of his team. In either event, have Whitecastle repeat his call to other player characters until they get the hint. If the thought of nuyen doesn't entice the characters, then they've been leading too easy a life. Let one or two of them be mugged, robbed, or become a victim of a computer theft, then see if they aren't suddenly interested in earning money. If all else fails, omit the entire first run of the adventure and go straight to rescuing Euphoria. In that unfortunate event, let the characters hang out for four days and then go straight to **Deja Vu**.

OFF AND RUNNING

TELL IT TO THEM STRAIGHT

The pier area is deserted by nine o'clock at night. If any of the characters try to hide in or around the dockside warehouses, read the following:

You wait patiently as eleven o'clock slowly approaches. The pier is quiet except for the sound of the ocean breeze whistling among the warehouses on the dock. Suddenly, a figure appears several meters from your hiding position.

"Easy chummer, I'm just checking the area for Mr. Johnson. Don't get itchy on me. I can understand you hombres wanting a lookout, but I can't bring in Mr. Johnson until everybody's on the pier. You've got to meet our trust halfway, my friend. Now let's all get together on the pier and we can talk business."

The man backs away around a corner and into the darkness.

Once all the characters in the dock area are assembled on the pier, continue with the following:

At eleven o'clock, Pier 36 is a lonely stretch of wooden planking stretching out into the bay. The only light comes from an incandescent street lamp on the road near the pier. The old light hangs by a frazzled cable and sways in the wind, throwing a cone of light up and down the pier. The shifting throws your shadows far down the pier where the waves are crashing in and then gathers them like dark pools around your feet. Over the sound of the wind and the waves, you hear a dull rumble approaching.

A razorguy slowly cruises onto the street about a block away and turns toward Pier 36. He has a Latin appearance and is decked out in black leather. His bike is a big Harley Scorpion urban combat bike, which he idles low as he rumbles along the pier. You can see that the bike is plated up and mounts an Ingram machine gun. As he rides toward you, the razorguy's eyes roam the nearby buildings and docks.

He brakes the Scorpion to a halt and slowly lifts his mirrored shades to examine your group. His red cybereyes blaze in the darkness. Giving the area one last check, he replaces his shades, rolls up his jacket sleeve, and punches a number into a wristphone. After whispering into the mike, he cancels the call and leans back on the bike seat, crossing his arms.

A moment later, a night blue Toyota Elite with opaque, tinted windows pulls into the street along the docks. It cruises silently up to the pier, stopping behind the Latin's idling Scorpion. The driver gets out and walks around to the rear door closest to you. He opens the door and steps back to let a sharply dressed man emerge from the Elite. As the man walks toward you, you know you haven't seen this Johnson before, but his is like a hundred other faces. His smooth hair and clear complexion are implant-perfect.

"Gentlemen, shall we talk business?" The man smiles broadly, but you get the distinct impression that the eyes behind his expensive shades aren't smiling. Those eyes are summing you up and slapping a price tag on your forehead.

"You may know that the simsense star Euphoria will make some public appearances in a few days to promote a Strice Foods product called Amber Gel. The interests I represent would prefer not to see such a talented and popular young lady promote that product. Therefore, something must be done to prevent this tragedy. That's where you, um, chummers, come into the picture. We'd like you to escort Euphoria away from public view for a few days and entertain her long enough that she misses her scheduled appearances.

"Of course, we are all great fans of Euphoria, and so we would not want to see her get hurt. Part of the deal is that *no* harm comes to the lady. Treat her like royalty. All you have to do is kidnap, um, detain, her and hold her for three days. I'm prepared to pay you up to 20,000 nuyen each. Half when you get Euphoria and the other half after she misses her last appearance. What do you gentlemen say?"

The characters can now bargain for the price. That done, read the following:

"Tomorrow is Thursday. Euphoria's appearances run Friday through Sunday. So you must take Euphoria tomorrow night. I'm sure she'll be in her penthouse until her first appearance Friday. She is rather reclusive, you know."

"Euphoria's place is on the twenty-first floor of Pacific Towers on Ward Street. Here is a keycard to the flat I've rented for your use in holding Euphoria. It's in the Redmond Barrens, and the address is on the keycard. You are registered under the name of John Smith, room number 812. You will receive half-payment Friday at the flat once I'm sure Euphoria has disappeared. The other half will be delivered Sunday after her last scheduled appearance comes and goes. You should release Euphoria then."

Mr. Johnson gives you a long look. "Do the job well, and everything will run smoothly. Remember, no harm to the girl."

He turns and walks back to the Elite. The chauffeur closes the door behind Johnson, then walks around to the other side and gets in. The blue Elite pulls away, becoming one with the night. The samurai on the Harley nods to you. "Good luck, chummers. If you need to contact us, my wrist number if 5-5-Chrome." He grips the handlebars and the bike roars to life. Taking off down the road, he follows the limo out of sight.

BEHIND THE SCENES

Pier 36 is located among the disreputable and dangerous areas of the Tacoma docks. The heavy wooden pier stretches out over the water for about a hundred meters. A road runs alongside the pier, stretching down the dock area. Across the street are several warehouses in various stages of disrepair. Most are empty near Pier 36, but those further along the road house squatters, gang hideouts, or illegal goods. Few ships use the docks in this area, and so the pier is deserted by nine at night. Lone Star doesn't even bother to patrol here.

Mr. Johnson, whose real name is unimportant, is an executive in Ludivenko's Seattle operations. (Use the **Mr. Johnson** Contact, p. 170, **SR** rules.)

Mr. Johnson offers the characters 20,000 nuyen each for the run, but as usual, this sum is open to negotiation. Mr. Johnson has Negotiation Skill 6. Make an Opposed Negotiation Test, with every extra success adding or subtracting 1,000 nuyen from the original offer. The only non-negotiable part of the deal is the payment plan, i.e., half after the abduction and half after Euphoria misses her last scheduled appearance.

Once the fee is settled, Mr. Johnson will discuss the details of the run. The characters are expected to kidnap Euphoria from her penthouse the following night and to hold her for three days in a rented apartment while her scheduled appearances come and go. Because Mr. Johnson wants to keep an eye on both the runners and the simstar, it will be hard to persuade him that Euphoria should be held anywhere but the rented apartment.

"Well, you, uhm, chummers can hold the lady anywhere you like, but your payments will be delivered to the rented flat."

Mr. Johnson will repeat that Euphoria must not be harmed. If she is injured or killed, Ludivenko will not be able to use her for their own ads.

Johnson will not reveal that he works for Ludivenko, though the characters may discover it anyway. He will try to answer any reasonable questions, but his manner is condescending, especially if the runners ask anything that he considers too obvious.

The Toyota Elite's driver is Johnson's bodyguard. (Use the **Company Man** Contact, page 164, **SR** rules.) He wears a Lined Coat, and is armed with a Browning Max-Power pistol with attached silencer and explosive ammo. He will attack only if the player characters become violent.

The razorguy is Juan Diablo, a gang punk turned samurai through Ludivenko's funding. Diablo will back up the Company Man if trouble breaks out. (Use the **Street Samural** stats for Diablo, page 46, **SR** rules, with Gunnery Skill 4.) He is armed with an Uzi III with shock pads and Smartgun Adapter, an armored vest with plates, and the weaponry on his Harley. Diablo gives the player characters his wristphone number in case they need to contact their employers.

The keycard is a normal plastic version with a magnetic strip. Printed on it is the address of Royal Meadows Apartments, the high-rise building where the hideout flat is located.

Now that the characters are ready to begin, they have several options. They may wish to hit the streets to dig up information on Euphoria, as covered in **Legwork**. If they decide to check out the Royal Meadows Apartments, go to **Royal What?** If they want to check out Pacific Towers or when they are ready to kidnap Euphoria, go to the **Pacific Towers** and **To Catch a Star** sections, respectively.

DEBUGGING

If some of the runner characters refuse to assemble on the pier, have Mr. Johnson come in anyway. Only the characters on the pier can participate in the negotiations. If the characters become violent, his chauffeur and Juan provide cover while he tries to escape. The deal will fall through. Go on to **Deja Vu** and have the characters hear about Euphoria's disappearance. Or, if the characters absolutely refuse to accept the deal, go on to **Deja Vu** anyway.

ROYAL WHAT?

TELL IT TO THEM STRAIGHT

When the players check out the apartment rented for them by Mr. Johnson, read the following:

You wouldn't believe it if the sign didn't confirm it. You're standing in front of Royal Meadows Apartments, but the meadows are conspicuously absent and there's nothing royal about the soot-covered building towering over you. Set on the edge of the Redmond Barrens, the building could easily pass for one of the Barrens' slum tenements. It is 18 stories of steel framework and concrete cinderblock polished up with plastic windows, rusted iron sculptures, and at least three decades of pollution and grime. A steady stream of wage slaves and street people pour in and out of the main doors.

The lobby area is everything you expected and less. A wide hallway leads to a nexus of elevators. Moving down the hall, you see a sign reading, "MANAGER", over a window set into the wall. Behind the heavy plastic window, you see a Dwarf reading the morning fax. Security amounts to one Ork fast asleep at his station down by the elevators.

Not trusting the elevators, you trudge up the eight flights of stairs, disturbing various forms of vermin, insect and otherwise, as you go.

You slot the keycard into the maglock on the door of apartment 812. The lock buzzes noisily and you hear a bolt slide. As the door opens, you expect the worst and you're right. Whatever corp runs this place sure knows how to cut corners. The three-room flat has a living area, bedroom, and bathroom. The bathroom is the size of a coffin, and you doubt whether the water filters have ever been changed. The bedroom has two doubles pushed so close that they look like one big mattress. The living room boasts out-of-date furniture made from low-grade plastic. Just off the living room is a closet-sized kitchenette with a couple of cupboards, a microwave, a sink, and a refrigerator. The air in the room is stale and thick. The insects in residence seem to eye you speculatively as though trying to decide whether to fight you for their turf. They don't. Yet.

BEHIND THE SCENES

If the runners are smart, they'll locate the rented flat before they make their run, so they don't have to stop and ask directions while they cart around a kidnapped star. Royal Meadows Apartments is an 18-floor corporate tenement located a few blocks into the Barrens. The building is in poor repair and is filthy. Unless the player characters have a lifestyle of Streets or Squatter, the apartment building will be far below the quality of their normal lodgings.

The landlord is Crucius Bunter. Crucius is the Dwarf behind the manager's window most hours of the day. He is about thirty-five, with a face pockmarked by disease. Irritable and overworked, Crucius is responsible for most of the building's maintenance. With too many rooms for one man to keep up, the place is slowly falling apart. Crucius has given up on most periodic maintenance jobs such as replacing water and air filters. If the characters complain to him about a maintenance problem, he will either mumble about getting to it or berate them for expecting so much and then launch into a tale of his woes. Nuyen talks, however, and even a little bribe will be enough to persuade Crucius to make some repairs.

The hideout apartment is number 812 and has been rented for the entire month under the name John Smith. Following is a room-by-room description of the flat. The characters are free to come and go as they please. The building offers no effective security checks.

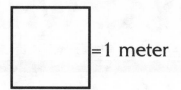

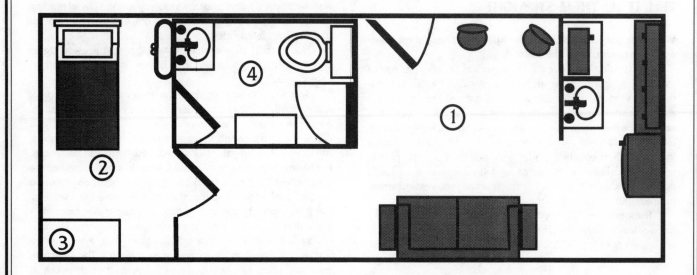

Royal Meadows

ROYAL MEADOWS FLAT MAP KEY

Living Room/Kitchenette (1)

The living room contains two chairs and a couch covered in black plastic. An end table is on either side of the couch, and a larger table sits in the room's center. All the tables are made from imitation wood. The kitchenette boasts a microwave unit, refrigerator, cupboards, and sink. The cupboards are stocked with sealed containers of dehydrated food, courtesy of Ludivenko. (If prepared correctly, these products are surprisingly tasty.) One of the chairs will break if used as a seat, and the freezer in the refrigerator does not work. The sink's water filters are disgusting, and the main air filter in the living room ceiling needs to be changed.

Bedroom (2)

The bedroom contains two double beds squeezed next to one another. Knowing that the rented units will be packed with people, the building owners have accommodated the over-crowding with more beds. The beds are made from hard plastic frames and foam mattresses. An imitation wood dresser with a plastic mirror stands in one corner. The dresser drawers contain a few items of women's clothing still in plastic wrap. Ludivenko has supplied them for Euphoria.

Closet (3)

Hanging here are several items of average size women's clothing. Ludivenko has provided these for Euphoria's use.

Bathroom (4)

This room has a shower stall, toilet, and sink. All the water filters need changing. The sink's hot water faucet does not work.

DEBUGGING

If by some chance, the runners annoy the manager, it will cost them about 100 nuyen to calm him down.

PACIFIC TOWERS

TELL IT TO THEM STRAIGHT

Pacific Towers juts into the gray sky over Rosemont Beach like a great ebony spike. The sides of the building are covered with black polymer, except where plastic-enclosed balconies extend out from the walls. The building is 25 stories high, each story slightly smaller than the one below, so that the structure tapers almost to a point. Four sets of doors face the street.

The building's lobby is magnificent. The floor is gray marble covered with a scattering of colorful woven rugs. The walls are also gray marble, and are hung with fine oil paintings. Your heart skips when you see that the ceiling vaults above you like a cathedral, but then you realize it is only a spatial illusion generated with holographs. Facing the front doors is a security station. One guard sits at a circular desk of gray marble and gold trim. Behind the security station are three elevators, and to the left is a restaurant/bar. To your right is a large store filled with clothing and electronics, and to the right are more doors.

BEHIND THE SCENES

To kidnap Euphoria, the characters have three choices. They can take her from her penthouse; they can capture her as she leaves the building; or they can seize her in transit to her first appearance. If they decide to try it *after* she arrives at the theatre, the runners will encounter all the risks of much heavier security. MegaMedia is especially security-conscious since the defection of megastar Honey Brighton to their Chicago-based rival, Brilliant Genesis.

TAKING EUPHORIA AT HOME

From the time the characters are hired until Euphoria must leave for her first appearance, she will remain in her 21st-floor penthouse. To kidnap Euphoria from here will mean finding a way to penetrate the apartment's security. They will probably make a frontal assault through the lobby, unless they can climb the outside walls or make an aerial entrance through Euphoria's greenhouse balcony. The gamemaster must use the information presented here and in the next section, **To Catch a Star**, to conduct the characters' invasion.

TAKING HER AT THE DOOR

When Euphoria exits the building on the way to her performance, she is escorted by Osprey and Stone. A pair of building guards (see **Pacific Towers Security Guard**, p. 15) are also watching the street. Osprey and Stone will take Euphoria directly to a Mitsubishi Nightsky waiting at the curb. The driver is a Knight Errant Securities man who is not a Rigger. (See **Knight Errant Security Guard**, p. 15.)

Osprey and Stone will ride with Euphoria in the Nightsky, while a second pair of Knight Errant guards lead in a modified Ford Americar. They proceed directly to the theatre.

TAKING HER ON THE ROAD

Going after Euphoria on the road will involve dealing with the Nightsky and its occupants, the Americar and its occupants, as well as any back-up the Knight Errant guards call in. If the guards have a chance to make it, a quick radio message will bring a Knight Errant Wasp helicopter to the scene in three minutes.

PACIFIC TOWERS BUILDING

Pacific Towers caters to corporate executives, who own or lease most of the building's condos. The building has 25 floors and 2 sublevels for parking. All 25 floors hold three or four condos, except for the top five floors, which consist of one penthouse condo each. Euphoria's 21st floor penthouse is the largest residence in the building, but it is rather small for a star of Euphoria's popularity and financial resources. However, Euphoria enjoys the accommodations and the professionalism of the building's staff, who respect her privacy.

A guard is on duty at the lobby desk all hours of the day (See **Pacific Towers Security Guard**.) A bellboy or courier is also on duty at all hours to fetch residents whatever they might need (Use **Corporate Wage Slave** Contact, p. 108, **Sprawl Sites**.) From the hours of 9:00 A.M. to 10:00 P.M., five other personnel are working at the building. These include a maintenance man, bartender, lifeguard, and two store clerks (Use **Wage Slave**, above.) There are generally some executives lounging at the bar or swimming in the pool, especially after 5:00 P.M. (Use **Corporate Official**, p. 107, **Sprawl Sites**.)

Security at Pacific Towers is not that tight, but it is difficult to slip through without raising an alarm. All visitors must check in with the guard on duty upon entering the building. The guards know all the residents and will question anyone unfamiliar about why they are on the premises. When a visitor checks in, a guard buzzes the resident for verification of the visitor over video. The guard then unlocks the elevators for the visitor and programs the lift for the proper floor.

Security cameras are stationed throughout the ground floor and in each elevator. The lobby guard monitors the cameras from his desk. The building also has its own computer system, which is not attached to the local matrix. The system controls the building's machinery and keeps records of scheduled visitors and other information for the guard.

There is no magical security.

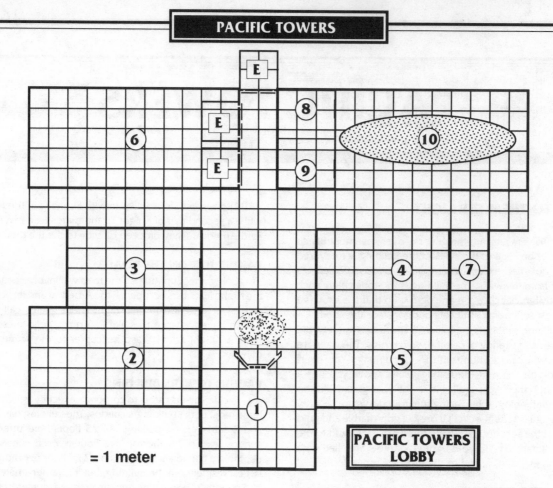

= 1 meter

PACIFIC TOWERS LOBBY

PACIFIC TOWERS MAP KEY

LOBBY

Front Entrance/Guard Station (1)

Four sets of double doors offer entrance to the building from Ward Street. The security station has a computer terminal, PANICBUTTON alarm, a camera and speaker for visitor-verification, and monitors for the building's security cameras. At night, the courier on duty will be here talking with the guard unless an errand takes the courier outside the building. The guard is armed as noted but also has access to a fully loaded Enfield AS7 shotgun kept behind his desk. The courier will not fight and has average Human statistics (all 3's).

If the guard hits the PANICBUTTON, four Lone Star officers will arrive in five minutes. (Use the **Street Cop** Contact, p. 171 **SR** rules.) All are armed with Browning Max-Power heavy pistols [8 (clip), 1 extra clip, 4M2], stun batons [+1 Reach, 5L2 Stun + Special damage], and Armor Vests [2/1]. The Lone Star officers will call for additional back-up if they meet resistance.

It is possible to phone in and cancel the PANICBUTTON alert. The caller must give a code, which every guard has memorized. The number to call and the cancellation code are stored in the building's computer system. If the alarm is cancelled before five minutes have elapsed, the patrol of four officers will not arrive.

Three elevators service the building. The elevator doors are locked with a thumbprint identifier. The lock will recognize any of the building's residents or employees. According to the thumbprint of the resident, the elevator will automatically be programmed for the correct floor. Building employees have access to all floors and manually select their destination. The elevator lock can be bypassed with a successful Electronics (5) Skill Test, with a base time of 5 minutes.

Bar (2)

This area is for use by the building's residents and their guests. It is little used during the day, but stays busy between the hours of five and ten in the evening.

Meeting Room (3)

This private meeting room is for corporate residents who wish to conduct business meetings closer to home.

Lecture Room (4)

This lecture room is used by corporate residents, doubling as a small theater for the residents at night.

Store (5)

Catering to the building residents, this store offers an extensive line of expensive clothing and entertainment electronics. The courier delivers purchases to residents so that they can shop without leaving their homes. The store also provides the morning datafax and other business necessities.

Garden (6)

This garden courtyard area is available for parties and business functions.

Storeroom (7)

Men's Restroom (8)

A sauna and shower are provided for pool-users.

Women's Restroom (9)

Same as men's.

Pool (10)

The pool is open at all hours for residents and guests. Each lounge chair has its own ultraviolet tanning light and gear.

PACIFIC TOWERS COMPUTER SYSTEM

The building's computer system consists of a small business computer wired to various heating and lighting sensors. There is no access to the building's computer from the Matrix. The only access is through the terminal at the lobby security desk.

I/OP-1: This is the security desk terminal. Green-3, Access 3

SM-1: This slave module controls all of the security cameras in the building. Orange-3, Barrier 3

SM-2: The slave module controls all heating and lighting for the building's general areas. Each condo has its own independent controls. The module also controls the elevators. A decker can open or close the elevator doors and send the elevators to any floor through the slave module. Orange-3, Access 4

DS-1: This datastore holds a lot of miscellaneous information. Records on visitors and needed maintenance jobs fill most of the datastore. The number and code for cancelling the PANICBUTTON alarm are also kept here. The number is 2206 (312-1876) and the operator who answers will request the code, which is J87. Green-3

CPU: Orange-4, Barrier 3.

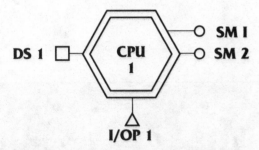

PACIFIC TOWERS COMPUTER SYSTEM

OTHER NPCS

PACIFIC TOWERS SECURITY GUARD

These guards are building security, barely trained and nearly inexperienced.

B	Q	S	C	I	W	E	M	R	Armor
4	3	3	2	2	2	6	—	2	2/1

Dice Pools: Defense (Armed) 1, Defense (Unarmed) 3, Dodge 3

Skills: Etiquette (Corporate) 2, Firearms 3, Unarmed Combat 3

Gear: Armor Vest (2/1), Ceska Black Scorpion [25 (clip), 1 extra clip, 3M2]

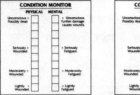

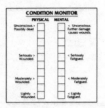

KNIGHT ERRANT SECURITY GUARD

Currently at a Group Three training level, these guards are a cut above the usual corporate security guard, but not elite.

B	Q	S	C	I	W	E	M	R	Armor
4	4	4	3	2	4	6	—	3	5/3

Dice Pools: Defense (Armed) 3, Defense (Unarmed) 4, Dodge 4

Skills: Armed Combat 3, Car 3, Etiquette (Corporate) 3, Firearms 4, Throwing 3, Unarmed Combat 4

Gear: Airfoil IPE Concussion Grenades (5M3 Stun), Ares Predator II [15 (clip), 2 extra clips, Laser Sight, 6M2), Armor Jacket (5/3)

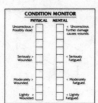

MITSUBISHI NIGHTSKY

Handling	Speed	Body	Armor	Signature	Pilot	Cost
4	45/120	5	1	4	4	250,000¥

Note: This particular Nightsky has no concealed weaponry.

VEHICLE

Type _____

	Rating	Condition Monitor
Handling	____	< Vehicle Destroyed
Speed,	____	
Body	____	
Armor	____	< Serious Damage
Signature	____	
Pilot	____	
Firmpoints	____	< Moderate Damage
Hardpoints	____	< Light Damage

FORD AMERICAR (SECURITY VARIANT)

Handling	Speed	Body	Armor	Signature	Pilot	Cost
4	45/135	3	1	2	2	80,000¥

Notes: Equipped with two-way radio.

VEHICLE

Type _____

	Rating	Condition Monitor
Handling	____	< Vehicle Destroyed
Speed,	____	
Body	____	
Armor	____	< Serious Damage
Signature	____	
Pilot	____	
Firmpoints	____	< Moderate Damage
Hardpoints	____	< Light Damage

NORTHRUP PRC-42D WASP

Handling	Speed	Body	Armor	Signature	Pilot	Cost
3	65/100	1	1	5	0	340,000¥

Weaponry: One (1) Light Machine Gun mounted under the nose. [LMG, 100 (Belt, internal), Laser Sight, 5S3] rigged for automatic 6 shots, no Recoil Modifier.

Note: The PRC-42d is a variant of the standard Wasp, with special Ares Armorflex™ vehicle armor. For the pilot, use the **Knight Errant Security Guard** above, but substitute Rotor for Car at the same value.

VEHICLE

Type _____

	Rating	Condition Monitor
Handling	____	< Vehicle Destroyed
Speed,	____	
Body	____	
Armor	____	< Serious Damage
Signature	____	
Pilot	____	
Firmpoints	____	< Moderate Damage
Hardpoints	____	< Light Damage

TO CATCH A STAR

GAMEMASTER'S NOTE: The following should be used initially if the runners attempt to kidnap Euphoria from her penthouse. The gamemaster will also need to refer to it later, following her second abduction.

BEHIND THE SCENES

Euphoria's 21st-floor condo is filled with luxuries of the high life in 2050. Though the condo's amenities and furnishings are the finest nuyen can buy, they are not ostentatious. Euphoria prefers an interior design based more on utility than appearance. The characters should end up visiting Euphoria's condo twice, once to abduct the star and a second time to investigate her second disappearance.

Preceding her public appearance schedule, security around Euphoria will increase. Strice Foods has hired a team of Knight Errant Security guards to provide extra protection for the simstar from the evening before her first scheduled appearance on Friday through Sunday evening. The security team stays at Euphoria's condo and receives orders from her personal bodyguard, Michael Adams. Adams, known by his operating name of Osprey, has recently brought in an old associate named Alexander Cross, or Stone. Cross is a Street Mage brought in for magical protection.

If the runners attack the condo, Osprey will order the Knight Errant Security team to repel any invaders while he checks to make sure that Euphoria is safe. Once Euphoria is out of direct danger, Osprey and Stone will support the security team. Euphoria will attempt to hide in her bedroom away from the action. She will be very cooperative with the player characters if threatened at all, though the runners may wish to drug her or knock her out anyway. If conscious, Euphoria will remain fearful and docile throughout the abduction. Once the characters arrive at the hideout with Euphoria, go on to the next chapter, **Holding Euphoria**.

DEBUGGING

If the characters lose the fight against Euphoria's security force, things are in sad shape for them. The gamemaster could decide to turn them over to Lone Star and start over with a new team at **Deja Vu**. If the characters have put up a good fight, he can also give them a chance to escape. If Osprey is conscious, he will interrogate the runners to find out who hired them and why. If they escape and salvage their run by taking Euphoria, go the the next chapter, **Holding Euphoria**. If they simply escape, Euphoria will make her first appearance at Renraku, where another team hired by Ludivenko will abduct her. The characters will have to wait around for a couple days and then go to **Deja Vu**.

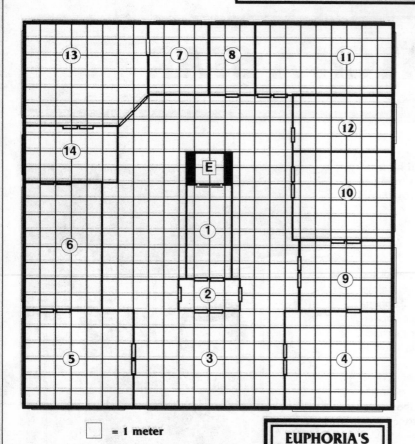

☐ = 1 meter

EUPHORIA'S CONDO

Recording Studio (4)

This is Euphoria's private recording studio. Though her sims are recorded on-location, she practices each scene in her studio before going out for the real take. The studio has a complete set of professional simsense gear here, including recorder, editing machine, and playback units. A desk is full of strong sensory materials such as sandpaper, incense, lemon juice, and so on, used to fine-tune the recording gear to Euphoria's nervous system. There are piles of strip printouts scattered around the room.

Greenhouse Balcony (5)

Euphoria's favorite place to relax is this balcony, which offers a nearly panoramic view of Seattle. The balcony is totally enclosed in a clear impact plastic (Barrier Rating 6). Tropical plants overflow the area, making the effect almost jungle-like. Hidden speakers are programmed to play recordings of rain and soft animal sounds. The view through the main windows can be replaced with holographic images of several different cities or natural environments.

Workout Room (6)

A star must be conscious of the shape she is in, and Euphoria is not content to let cosmetic surgery do all the work. She puts herself through a rigorous aerobic exercise program every day. The room contains mats, hydraulic resistance machines, and a small hot tub.

Closet (7)
Bathroom (8)
Kitchen (9)

Euphoria does not employ any servants not absolutely necessary. She prepares her own meals in this fully automated kitchen. Groceries are delivered.

Dining Room (10)

Used only for business lunches, or dinners.

Osprey's Bedroom (11)

This room is beautifully furnished in an English motif. It has a tapestry displaying the coat-of-arms of Michael Adams' supposed ancestors, posters of London and Stonehenge, and an antique cavalry sword from the Napoleonic Wars.

Spare Bedroom (12)

Stone is currently using this room. Very few of Stone's personal belongings are here, however.

Master Bedroom (13)

This is Euphoria's bedroom. It features a king-size bed made with real oak and the finest mattress foams, two dressers, and a vanity. In one corner is a full-figure projector, a 2050 mirror for the rich. The person stands on a small platform to see a full-scale holograph projected on a wall screen. The holograph can be rotated for a 360-degree view of oneself. The closet doors are an opaque image of the room's wall. Pressing a button makes the image drop to reveal Euphoria's immense wardrobe.

Master Bathroom (14)

The bathroom is tiled in white ceramic. It has luxury utilities.

EUPHORIA'S PENTHOUSE MAP KEY

Entrance Hall (1)

The building's elevators open onto this short hallway, where one of the four Knight Errant guards is stationed. Double doors open to the condo itself. The doors are locked, requiring an appropriate credstick to open. Bypassing the lock requires an Electronics (4) Test, with a base time of two minutes. The doors have a Barrier Rating of 5.

Foyer (2)

Inset into the wall near the entrance doors are a speaker and monitor that tie into the condo's security station. The gear is used to verify visitors. The foyer is decorated with some framed Monet prints and organic flowering plants.

Living Room (3)

This is the largest room in the condo. Euphoria uses it to entertain company on the rare occasion when she has guests. Several plush couches are arranged in a circle, and several sculptures, both holographic and real, are placed about. An entertainment center dominates one corner of the room. The center has a large trideo screen, an old laser disc player, a chip player, and several simsense playback units. Near the entrance to the balcony is a telecom station that doubles as Euphoria's desk. Euphoria's agent, Robert Carrone, handles almost all business, however, so the desk collects dust. Three Knight Errant guards are here.

OTHER NPCS

KNIGHT ERRANT SECURITY GUARDS

There are four security men on duty guarding Euphoria at all times. The team is very professional and will follow Osprey's instructions without hesitation. When Euphoria travels, two of the guards will precede her vehicle in a modified Ford Americar, one drives her Nightsky, and one remains behind in the condo. (See **Pacific Towers**, p. 13.)

Attributes
- Body: 4
- Quickness: 4
- Strength: 4
- Charisma: 3
- Intelligence: 2
- Willpower: 4
- Essence: 6
- Reaction: 3

Skills
- Armed Combat: 3
- Car: 3
- Etiquette (Corporate): 3
- Firearms: 4
- Throwing: 3
- Unarmed Combat: 4

Dice Pools
- Defense (Armed): 3
- Defense (Unarmed): 4
- Dodge: 4

Cyberware
- None

Gear
- (2) Airfoil IPE Concussion Grenades (5M3 Stun)
- Ares Predator II [15 (clip), 2 extra clips, Laser Sight, 6M2]
- Armor Jacket (5/3)
- H&K MP-5TX [20 (clip), 2 extra clips, Laser Sight, 4M3]

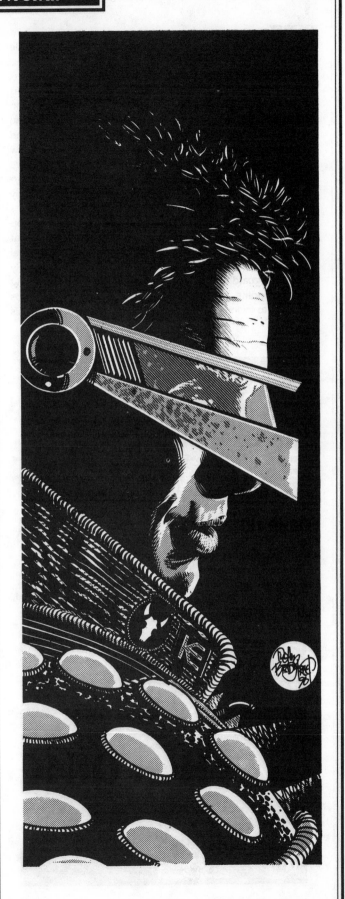

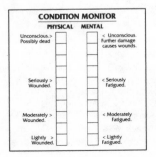

CONDITION MONITOR

PHYSICAL	MENTAL
Unconscious.> Possibly dead	< Unconscious. Further damage causes wounds.
Seriously > Wounded.	< Seriously Fatigued.
Moderately > Wounded.	< Moderately Fatigued.
Lightly > Wounded.	< Lightly Fatigued.

CONDITION MONITOR

PHYSICAL	MENTAL
Unconscious.> Possibly dead	< Unconscious. Further damage causes wounds.
Seriously > Wounded.	< Seriously Fatigued.
Moderately > Wounded.	< Moderately Fatigued.
Lightly > Wounded.	< Lightly Fatigued.

CONDITION MONITOR

PHYSICAL	MENTAL
Unconscious.> Possibly dead	< Unconscious. Further damage causes wounds.
Seriously > Wounded.	< Seriously Fatigued.
Moderately > Wounded.	< Moderately Fatigued.
Lightly > Wounded.	< Lightly Fatigued.

CONDITION MONITOR

PHYSICAL	MENTAL
Unconscious.> Possibly dead	< Unconscious. Further damage causes wounds.
Seriously > Wounded.	< Seriously Fatigued.
Moderately > Wounded.	< Moderately Fatigued.
Lightly > Wounded.	< Lightly Fatigued.

OSPREY

Michael Adams was born in England and moved to Seattle when his father took a job with Renraku. Michael enjoyed slumming as a youngster and grew up as much on the streets as in his parents' comfortable corporate shelter. When he was in his late teens, a rival corporation extracted his father and mother from Renraku. Michael used the money that Renraku paid to support him to purchase some cyber modifications, and went to work on the streets as a samurai-for-hire. After a few years of shadowrunning, he gave up the biz in favor of more secure employment. His good looks landed him several bodyguard assignments, and he eventually wound up with a steady job protecting Euphoria for MegaMedia.

Guarding Euphoria is a stressful job. Simstars develop fanatic followings, and some fans so identify with the star that they want to become that person. This, of course, means the real star must die so that the lunatic fan can become the one and only star. While guarding Euphoria, Osprey has had to do everything from defending her from entire gangs to defusing bombs intended to incinerate her. Osprey charges a high price for his services.

He is taller than average, with a slender but muscular frame. He has dirty blonde hair and pale blue eyes. Osprey has avoided modifications that would mar his appearance so as not to detract from the glamorous appearance of any stars he might guard.

Though Osprey has been with Euphoria for some time, he has not developed any special friendship with her. Beneath Osprey's veneer of culture and gentility is a mercenary ruthlessness. He is proud of his English heritage and accentuates it in various ways. When he is off-duty, slumming is still a favorite pastime.

Adams is loyal to MegaMedia because they fill his credstick. He must often babysit Euphoria to keep her from running off and avoiding her job duties. Euphoria does not appreciate Osprey being a watchdog more loyal to MegaMedia than to her.

Attributes
Body: 5
Quickness: 5
Strength: 4
Charisma: 5
Intelligence: 4
Willpower: 5
Essence: .3
Reaction: 5 (9)

Skills
Armed Combat: 5
Car: 3
Demolitions: 2
Etiquette (Corporate): 2
Etiquette (Media): 4
Etiquette (Street): 4
Firearms: 7
Interrogation: 3
Leadership: 2
Negotiation: 4
Stealth: 5
Unarmed Combat: 5

Dice Pools
Defense (Armed): 5
Defense (Unarmed): 5
Dodge: 5

Cyberware
(2) Chipjacks
Datasoft Link
Retinal Modification with Thermographic and Flare Compensation
Retractable Razors
Skillwire (6)
Skillsoft:
    Car (4)
    Demolitions (4)
    French (4)
    Interrogation (5)
    Japanese (4)
    Monofilament Whip (5)
Smartgun Link
Wired Reflexes (2)

Gear
Armor Jacket (5/3)
BMW 330LS sportscar
Colt Manhunter [16 (clip), 1 extra clip, Smartgun Link, 4M2]
FN HAR [20 (clip), 2 extra clips, Smartgun Adapter, Gas Vent (2), Explosive Ammunition, 5M3]
    Monofilament Whip (+2 Reach, 6S4)
    Pocket Secretary
    Wristphone

CONDITION MONITOR

	PHYSICAL		MENTAL	
Unconscious.> Possibly dead				< Unconscious. Further damage causes wounds.
Seriously > Wounded.				< Seriously Fatigued.
Moderately > Wounded.				< Moderately fatigued.
Lightly > Wounded.				< Lightly Fatigued.

STONE

Alexander Cross was born and raised on the streets of Seattle. His father was a sarariman and his mother a corporate secretary. Before his parents sent him off to UCLA for a college education, Alex ran with gangs. He gave his parents quite a surprise when he decided to major in magic instead of corporate finance. Rather than becoming a wage slave upon graduation, he sold his skills as a shadowrunner, teaming up with Osprey on several jobs. He retired from running shortly after Osprey did, and until recently worked in a public library as a hermetic consultant.

Alexander is tall and slightly overweight after a few relatively calm years. He has curly brown hair and heavy sideburns. Cross earned the name Stone because of his quiet and stoic demeanor. He is also a bit more noble-hearted than his associate Osprey.

As he is being employed to guard Euphoria, he will stand by her.

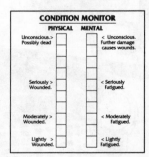

Attributes
- Body: 4
- Quickness: 2
- Strength: 3
- Charisma: 4
- Intelligence: 5
- Willpower: 6
- Essence: 6
- Magic: 6
- Reaction: 4

Skills
- Armed Combat (Clubs): 4
- Conjuring: 5
- Etiquette (Street): 3
- Firearms: 3
- Magical Theory: 8
- Sorcery: 7
- Stealth: 2
- Unarmed Combat: 2

Dice Pools
- Astral: 18
- Defense (Armed): 4
- Defense (Unarmed): 2
- Dodge: 2
- Magic: 7

Gear
- Armor Clothing (3/0)
- Browning Max-Power [8 (clip), 2 extra clip, Silencer, 4M2]
- 6 Expendable Manipulation Fetishes
- Staff [+2 Reach, 3M2 Stun]

Spells
- **Combat:**
  - Mana Bolt: 5
  - Powerball: 5
  - Sleep: 6
- **Detection:**
  - Detect Enemies: 3
- **Health:**
  - Increase Strength +2: 4
  - Treat Severe Wounds: 5
- **Manipulation (all known requiring Expendable Fetish):**
  - Armor: 8
  - Control Thoughts: 5
  - Petrify: 6

Notes: Stone has three Elementals bound into service:

Fire Elemental Force 5 assigned to Euphoria to provide her with Spell Defense.

Fire Elemental Force 4 bound to him. Stone uses it to aid him in casting Combat Spells.

Earth Elemental Force 5, which Stone uses to sustain an Armor Spell before going into the thick of combat.

CONDITION MONITOR	
PHYSICAL	**MENTAL**
Unconscious.> Possibly dead	< Unconscious. Further damage causes wounds.
Seriously > Wounded.	< Seriously Fatigued.
Moderately > Wounded.	< Moderately Fatigued.
Lightly > Wounded.	< Lightly Fatigued.

HOLDING EUPHORIA

TELL IT TO THEM STRAIGHT

Wow! Euphoria's everything you simmed about her and more. She's glamorous and beautiful beyond imagination. You've seen so many fabulous places through her eyes, or else you've been there with her through her male co-star, Hans Vandenburg. And now, she's right here with you in person. It's too much to believe. She returns your stare with obvious fear.

BEHIND THE SCENES

Once the characters seize Euphoria and make their getaway to the rented flat, things will wind down somewhat. Euphoria will remain docile and frightened until she believes that the characters do not intend to harm her. Over the three days that the characters hold Euphoria, she will gradually open up to them and reveal her true character. She is basically a spoiled child at heart and becomes quite a nag as the weekend goes on. "I'm supposed to sleep in *that* bed. But it's full of *bugs*!"

Described below are several events or encounters that occur during the three days. Let the characters set up shop in the flat and then throw these things at them over the course of the weekend.

MISSED APPEARANCES

Once it is clear that the characters intend to hold Euphoria throughout her performance dates, Euphoria cheers up considerably. "Oh good, I really didn't want to face all those people. Have you ever been in front of a crowd of fans? Well, no, I guess you wouldn't know it, but it's so depressing. Seeing all those people milling about like cattle idolizing me because they can't face their own pathetic lives."

NO AMBER GEL

There is no Amber Gel in the flat because Ludivenko supplied the food that is stocked in the flat's kitchenette. Euphoria will ask kindly if someone could go out and purchase some. If no one goes, she will bide her time. Later, she will cozy up to one of the characters and begin to pout about not having anything to eat. If all else fails, she will throw a tantrum. Amber Gel does not contain any addictive substances. Euphoria just craves it.

AMBER GEL

If the players get some Amber Gel, they will, inevitably, try some or watch Euphoria do so. When they do, read the following to a magician among them. Only one character will

see the bizarre event transpire. If more than one magician is in the group, a Shaman is most eligible to see the Ants, then a Street Shaman, and then any Hermetic Mage. This strange occurrence is here solely to create suspense in the players' minds. It is simply one of those astral side effects of the Ant totem, similar to Craft's premonitions of doom in **The Prologue**.

"Well, it's time to try this stuffer that's getting so much attention. You watch as a teammate unscrews the lid of a jar of luscious Amber Gel and opens it. Immediately, tiny scurrying creatures pour out of the container all over your teammate's hands. In an instant, they blanket his hands in a writhing mass. You step forward to help your mate as he begins to bring his hand up to his mouth to feast on the swarm covering his hands. He must be oblivious to the danger. You knock the jar out of his one hand and grab the other as it approaches his mouth. The little creatures, ants, millions of them, crawl down from his hand onto yours, stinging you. And then your friend knocks you aside, shouting at you. You blink and realize that somehow, you had slipped into, what? Astral Perception?. Returning to your normal senses, you look down at the Amber Gel jar lying on the floor. A blue creamy mixture has spilled out onto the ground. You see some of the gel on your teammate's hands, as well as your own. You shake your head and blink your eyes, wondering if you need more sleep. And then your hand begins to ache. You scrape away the Amber Gel and look at your hand. The back of it is marred by a tiny red inflammation, like an insect bite."

WORD ON THE STREET

If any character leaves the flat during the three days, whether to get Euphoria some Amber Gel or for any other reason, he will hear talk on the street about the kidnapping. The gamemaster could make available to the characters the **Player Hand-out**, which is a print article concerning Euphoria's disappearance. If anyone wants to check with Contacts to see how much anyone really knows about the kidnapping, go to the **Legwork** section, p.56.

FIRST PAYMENT

On Friday morning, the characters receive their first payment at the flat. Go to **Payday** for the delivery.

ATTACK

On Sunday afternoon, the flat is attacked by Pride and his men, who were hired by Vincent Burroughs to find Euphoria. Go to **I've Got Pride** to conduct the combat.

5-5-CHROME

After Pride's attack, the characters will have to relocate. They should contact Juan Diablo to let him know where they have gone and where Diablo can deliver the last half of the characters' pay.

RELEASE

On Sunday afternoon, the players can release Euphoria.

FINAL PAYMENT

Once the characters have freed Euphoria, Diablo will deliver the rest of their fee on uncertified credsticks. To discourage the characters from ransoming the star, Ludivenko will withhold payment until Euphoria is set free.

DEBUGGING

Not much can go wrong in this section, but the runners will probably come up with something.

TELL IT TO THEM STRAIGHT

You're whiling the time away checking and rechecking your guns. On the bright side, you're getting paid well to stay at this dump, and you don't get to babysit simstars too often. You jump slightly at the knock on the door, then go over to peer through the peephole. Standing in the hall is a short man wearing an overcoat and a hat several sizes too large. You open the door just a crack and say, "Whaddaya want?"

The man doesn't reply immediately. He slowly leans forward and whispers, "Jack Sprat could eat no fat," then whirls around and scans the hallway as though he might have been followed. Then he leans forward again and continues, "And his wife could eat no lean." He nods at you as though sharing a secret, and then he opens his hand to reveal several credsticks. "I am just here to check the plumbing," he says loudly, trying to sound casual as he points to the credsticks and winks at you.

"Um…hello. I was sent by…" He pauses, unrolls a sheet of paper, and reads, "Mr. Johnson." He tucks the paper away. "My name is Vernon Gruder. I'm to deliver these credsticks."

BEHIND THE SCENES

Well, everyone makes mistakes, and Ludivenko's Mr. Johnson isn't perfect. He chose an overly adventuresome wage slave named Vernon Gruder to deliver the characters' first payment. Vernon is an interoffice courier for Ludivenko. (Use **Corporate Wage Slave**, p. 108, **Sprawl Sites**.) Vernon carries one certified credstick for each character, with the appropriate sum on each stick.

Vernon appears at the flat at about 10:00 A.M. Friday morning. He is dressed in a large overcoat and an even larger hat. He is so excited about his clandestine errand that he takes everything too far. He assumes anything the characters say is in code, and he reads two or three meanings into the simplest comment. "Do you want some soykaf before you go?" "Oh, soykaf, right, right. No I'm not allowed to carry a gun, I mean soykaf. It's against company policy." If he gets really excited, Vern will also throw out some more useless passwords, such as his nursery rhyme.

Poor Vernon is totally harmless. The characters can even milk him for information if they can get past his idiotic double-talk and confusion. Vern knows all the information given under Ludivenko in the **Legwork** section. Characters will need to make an Interrogation or Etiquette (Corp) Skill Test at Target Number 3. If Vern is physically threatened, the Target Number for Interrogation Rolls drops to 2.

If Vern is allowed to see Euphoria, he will go absolutely out of control, fawning over her, reminiscing about scenes from her sims, and lavishing praise on her. The characters will almost have to throw Vern out to tear him away from Euphoria.

DEBUGGING

Any mistreatment of Vern may get back to Mr. Johnson and Ludivenko and affect future employment. Hey, ya gotta be a professional round the clock. Dig?

I'VE GOT PRIDE

TELL IT TO THEM STRAIGHT

You're listening to Euphoria complain about the flat. It's enough to drive any sane man to chips. Ah well, the price of—

A sound in the hallway outside attracts your attention. You try forcing yourself to relax, but something's wrong. You grab your gear and tell Euphoria to hide. Too late.

The door comes flying apart in an explosion of particle board and splinters. Standing in the doorway are several men dressed in dapper street clothes. They're armed. Behind them stands a huge man with black skin. The man roars like a beast and charges into the room. Hell has broken loose.

BEHIND THE SCENES

On Sunday morning, at about 9:00 A.M., the hideout flat is attacked by men Vincent Burroughs of Strice Food has hired to find Euphoria. The group is led by an African called Pride. Pride used Ritual Sorcery and strands of Euphoria's hair picked up at her penthouse to track the star to the flat. With Pride are four Strice Foods guards brought in to provide some muscle. The men will shatter the front door of the flat and barge in with guns blazing. They will not harm Euphoria, but anything else warm and moving is fair game. All four men carry stun batons to incapacitate Euphoria if she causes problems.

After the combat, the characters will probably want to relocate. They are free to rent any kind of place that is appropriate or to stay in their own residences. The rest of their stay with Euphoria will be relatively uneventful. They will have to contact Diablo to get their second payment delivered, and they should drop Euphoria off in a reputable part of town.

DEBUGGING

If the runners were smart enough to set up a local security or perimeter watch, they may waylay Pride and his group before they reach the flat. If so, any combat should be waged in the halls of the building, as seems logical.

If the characters lose the combat, they remain in the flat and Euphoria is set free to make her remaining Sunday appearances. Luckily for the characters, Pride has told no one of Euphoria's whereabouts, preferring to handle the entire job himself. The characters are thus free to recover in the flat, though Crucius Bunter, the landlord, may have some questions about room damage. Salvage what's left of the team and go on to **Deja Vu**.

OTHER NPCS

THE STRICE BOYS

As Guards for one of Strice's many facilities, this is the closest these boys have ever come to real action. They may live to regret it.

B	Q	S	C	I	W	E	M	R	Armor
5	3	4	2	3	3	6	—	3	4/3

Dice Pools: Defense (Armed) 4, Defense (Unarmed) 4, Dodge 3

Skills: Armed Combat 4, Etiquette (Corporate) 2, Etiquette (Street) 2, Firearms 3, Stealth 2, Unarmed Combat 4

Gear: Armor Vest With Plates (4/3), Seco LD 120 [12 (clip), 1 extra clip, 3M2] Stun Baton [+1 Reach, 5L2 Stun + Special], Uzi III [16 (clip), 1 extra clip, Laser Sight, 4M3]

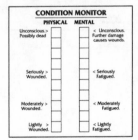

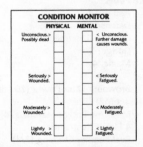

CONDITION MONITOR	
PHYSICAL	MENTAL
Unconscious.> Possibly dead	< Unconscious. Further damage causes wounds.
Seriously > Wounded.	< Seriously Fatigued.
Moderately > Wounded.	< Moderately Fatigued.
Lightly > Wounded.	< Lightly Fatigued.

CONDITION MONITOR	
PHYSICAL	MENTAL
Unconscious.> Possibly dead	< Unconscious. Further damage causes wounds.
Seriously > Wounded.	< Seriously Fatigued.
Moderately > Wounded.	< Moderately Fatigued.
Lightly > Wounded.	< Lightly Fatigued.

CONDITION MONITOR	
PHYSICAL	MENTAL
Unconscious.> Possibly dead	< Unconscious. Further damage causes wounds.
Seriously > Wounded.	< Seriously Fatigued.
Moderately > Wounded.	< Moderately Fatigued.
Lightly > Wounded.	< Lightly Fatigued.

CONDITION MONITOR	
PHYSICAL	MENTAL
Unconscious.> Possibly dead	< Unconscious. Further damage causes wounds.
Seriously > Wounded.	< Seriously Fatigued.
Moderately > Wounded.	< Moderately Fatigued.
Lightly > Wounded.	< Lightly Fatigued.

PRIDE

Shaka Jubowei was named after the great African conqueror Shaka Zulu. Jubowei grew up in Africa, learning the magic of the Sixth World from shamans who still carry on ancient traditions. He left his primitive home to make a name for himself in the modern world. He soon learned that a man with his abilities and savagery could reap considerable profit from selling his services. Taking the operating name of Pride, Jubowei became a globally active shadowrunner, specializing in bounty-hunting.

Pride stands almost two meters tall, with a muscular frame. His skin is very black, and his hair is long and stringy and grows all down the back of his neck. His eyes have vertical pupils like a cat's. He usually wears real leather clothing of African design.

Pride behaves like an aristocrat, but he is always cunning and becomes savage when angered. Pride gives no quarter in combat.

Attributes

Body: 6
Quickness: 5
Strength: 6
Charisma: 4
Intelligence: 4
Willpower: 6
Essence: 6
Magic: 6
Reaction: 5

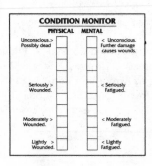

CONDITION MONITOR			
PHYSICAL		MENTAL	
Unconscious.> Possibly dead			< Unconscious. Further damage causes wounds.
Seriously > Wounded.			< Seriously Fatigued.
Moderately > Wounded.			< Moderately Fatigued.
Lightly > Wounded.			< Lightly Fatigued.

Skills

Armed Combat: 4
Etiquette (Corporate): 1
Etiquette (Street): 2
Etiquette (Tribal): 4
Firearms: 3
Magical Theory: 5
Negotiation: 4
Sorcery (Ritual): 6
Stealth: 5
Thrown Weapon (Spear): 6
Unarmed Combat: 5

Dice Pools

Astral: 14
Defense (Armed): 4
Defense (Unarmed): 5
Dodge: 5
Magic: 4

Gear

Browning Ultra-Power [10 (clip), Laser Sight, Firepower Ammo, 6M2]
Medicine Lodge Materials (4)
4 Plastic Restraints
Real Leather Clothing (2/1)
Spear [+2 reach, 6S3]
Survival Knife [6L3]

Spells

Combat:
Power Missile: 5
Fireball: 5
Detection:
Detect Enemies: 3
Mind Probe: 6
Health:
Detox Deadly Toxin: 5
Illusion:
Entertainment: 3

Notes

Pride's totem is Lion (see below).

LION TOTEM

Characteristics: Lion is the brave and powerful warrior. His method is direct and pointed, he is not a creature of subtlety, but prefers direct methods. Lion prefers to work from surprise and ambush, allowing others to perform tasks for him while reserving his strength. He will take the forefront if needed. Threaten his kin or family and you've threatened him.

Environment: Prairie

Advantages: +2 dice for Combat Spells; +2 dice for Prairie Spirits.

Disadvantages: −1 die for Health Spells. Lion is vain and gives special care to his physical condition and appearance. He must live well and demands respect and loyalty from those around him.

DEJA VU

TELL IT TO THEM STRAIGHT

GAMEMASTER'S NOTE: Read the following to the same player as in the opening chapter:

You wake up to the sound of your wristphone chirping away in the darkness. Your head pounds and your mouth feels like something between cotton and sandpaper. You have dim visions of a bartender who called himself Clockwork and had bright orange hair in a short spike. He wore a large medallion with a small vidscreen on it that constantly played some violent English film from the last century. Clockwork served you something called Rippers late into the night as you celebrated your recent income. Now your head is throbbing and it feels as though your brain is going to explode out of your skull. You promise yourself to practice some restraint the next time you celebrate.

You grope for your wristphone, which is lying somewhere in the dark. You grab it and clear your throat. Thumbing the receive switch, you give a hoarse croak, "Yeah".

The flip-up vidscreen shows Ellery Whitecastle dressed in a smoking jacket. He fidgets nervously with a pipe. "Hello chummer. Look, we've got a bit of a problem. MegaMedia somehow discovered that you were behind that temporary disappearance of Euphoria. So far, they're peaceful. They want you to meet with Robert Carrone, her manager, at the Pacific Towers lobby at eleven o'clock this morning. It's possible that they will excuse our involvement in the affair if you slip them any information you have on our former employers. Have your team meet with Carrone at eleven at Pacific Towers. At least see what he has to say. I'll be in touch as necessary."

The screen dies to a blip of green light and folds away automatically. A door opens and light frames a large man. The overhead lights sputter on in your room and you see the big guy has orange hair and a medallion shouting something about Beethoven. "Have a good nap, mate? Time for you to be leaving, I'm afraid. Come back soon." Clockwork shows you to the back door of the storage room, where you apparently spent the night.

BEHIND THE SCENES

Whitecastle has been contacted by MegaMedia who has discovered, through their street contacts, that he and the characters were responsible for kidnapping Euphoria. Now that Euphoria has disappeared again, MegaMedia "representatives" have applied more pressure to Whitecastle. The corp believes that the characters may have information about who has taken Euphoria a second time, or else some good guesses about who did and why. They are pressuring Whitecastle to make sure the characters come to meet with Robert Carrone to discuss the disappearances.

Carrone, as Euphoria's manager, has been given the job of recovering her. Both his career and hers are on the line. For the moment, he has decided to meet and deal with the runners on reasonable terms. Having spoken with Euphoria following her first kidnapping, he knows the runners did not mistreat her.

The characters should meet with Carrone at eleven o'clock at the Pacific Towers lobby. When it is time, go to **Meeting Carrone**.

It should be noted that the mass media has yet to learn of Euphoria's second disappearance.

DEBUGGING

If the runners fail to attend the meeting, they will receive another urgent call from Whitecastle. If they still refuse to meet Euphoria's manager, Carrone will send several Knight Errant guards employed by MegaMedia.

The guards will resort to force if necessary.

TELL IT TO THEM STRAIGHT

You're a little nervous when you enter Pacific Towers, but the guard doesn't give you any problems. You tell him you're to meet Robert Carrone in the lobby. He points to the left and politely tells you that Mr. Carrone is waiting at a table near the bar. You thank him and go around to the bar. The area is deserted except for a tall, lanky man in a gray business suit. The man sits motionless, brooding over the drink that rests on the table in front of him. He has red hair combed in a conservative corporate style, and opaque sunglasses rest atop his thin, hawk-like nose. As you approach, he shifts in his chair and scrutinizes you.

"Glad you could make it, gentlemen," he says. "Anyone want a drink? You'll need it." After the bartender delivers drinks to your table, the red-haired man motions you to follow through a side door into a small meeting room. When all of you have entered the room, he closes the door and locks it. He walks around the table and sits down, setting his drink in front of him. He flips on a White Noise Generator in the middle of the table, which comes to life with a dull hum.

"I'm Robert Carrone. I am a Vice President at MegaMedia in charge of Euphoria's career. I was her manager for many years before the MegaMedia contract, so my interest is personal as well as professional. As you are well aware, Euphoria disappeared last weekend. That kidnapping severely affected her earnings this month because it caused a profitable deal with Strice Foods to fall through. But that's history, and I don't like to deal with the past. Unfortunately, it seems that history is about to repeat itself.

"Another big corporation, who shall remain nameless, has contracted with Euphoria for another advertising campaign. Now Euphoria has disappeared again. If we don't find her by this weekend—assuming she still lives—then this second advertising contract will be voided.

"You people are not too popular with MegaMedia these days because of your involvement in the first kidnapping. Corporate business is handled by men of education and status. When street people like you attempt to dictate the flow of business in the corporate world, you anger those corporations. Your corporate employer for the extraction has settled its debt with us, as will your friend, Ellery Whitecastle." Carrone stops and looks at his watch. "Excuse me, as did your *late* friend, Mr. Whitecastle. It is time now for you to clean your slate with MegaMedia, and make nuyen doing it.

"Euphoria has been kidnapped again from her condo. Because I thought you might know what has happened to her, I decided to offer you the job of finding her, rather than trying to interrogate you. Find her and bring her back before this Saturday. I can offer each of you 20,000 nuyen for the job or half

that amount if Euphoria is returned later than 6 A.M. Saturday morning. Take the job, and MegaMedia will forget your involvement in the first kidnapping. Refuse it, and all I can promise is what Mr. Whitecastle received some fifteen minutes ago." **Stop here and negotiate the payment for the run.**

"As I said, Euphoria has been taken from her condominium here in Pacific Towers. MegaMedia extended Strice Foods' contract with Knight Errant Security to make sure that Euphoria was safe until they could find a bodyguard to replace Osprey. Unfortunately, the Knight Errant men were not sufficient protection. I think we should go up to the condominium and let you begin your search there. Virtually nothing has been touched since we discovered she was gone.

"Finally, none of this is to leak out to the press. Publicity around this event could cause Euphoria's current corporate sponsor to back out of their advertising agreement. MegaMedia will take care of explaining the disappearances of the Knight Errant security team."

BEHIND THE SCENES

MegaMedia has signed a contract with Ludivenko for Euphoria to do several promotions for Blue Bacosoy. When Carrone came to visit Euphoria to explain the new contract, he discovered that she had apparently been abducted from her condominium once again. Carrone immediately set events in motion to reclaim Euphoria. MegaMedia had, meanwhile, discovered Ludivenko's involvement in the first abduction, but they chose not to retaliate in return for a contract with Ludivenko for Euphoria's services. Ludivenko also supplied MegaMedia with the names of Whitecastle and the player characters so that the corp could exact its vengeance.

Carrone suspected that perhaps Whitecastle or the characters would know something about the second abduction, and so has hired the characters. He had Whitecastle interrogated and then killed when it was obvious that he knew nothing about the second abduction. Carrone is confident that the combination of threats and nuyen will make the characters bring in Euphoria if they do know anything. The runners, of course, know nothing about Euphoria's second disappearance, but as long as Carrone thinks they do, he wants them working on the case.

Carrone will pay each team member 20,000 nuyen or half that amount if Euphoria is returned later than Saturday at 6 A.M. The Saturday deadline is due to the deadlines for recording the Ludivenko advertisements. The characters can negotiate the 20,000 nuyen sum, as normal, with each extra success modifying the result by plus or minus 1,000 nuyen. Carrone will not reveal that Euphoria's new contract is with Ludivenko, saying that it is confidential business. He will insist on secrecy throughout the run to prevent Ludivenko from getting cold feet.

Carrone will also insist on full progress reports every eight hours. No exceptions.

Carrone's thumbprint will activate the lobby elevators for Euphoria's floor. He will take the characters up to the penthouse to have a look around. Go to **Missing Again** when the characters reach the condo. When the characters hit the streets once more, they will hear of Whitecastle's death as the result of a firebomb explosion at his residence. The body was identified by dental records.

DEBUGGING

If the characters refuse the job or attack Carrone, they will face corporate vengeance. The adventure will be over for them unless the gamemaster can find some way of reintegrating them into the plotline. Perhaps Euphoria will escape the Hive before undergoing her change, but with too much information for Craft to let her to live. Perhaps they know someone who the Hive has kidnapped for use as a host. Perhaps they witness the kidnapping, or perhaps, by some odd twist of fate, they are themselves the target.

MISSING AGAIN

TELL IT TO THEM STRAIGHT

You buzz up the elevator through Pacific Towers. The elevator glides to a halt and the doors open into the 21st-floor entrance hallway. The main door into Euphoria's condo is slightly ajar. A chair sits in the hallway with a cup of cold soykaf on the floor beside it. Everything is quiet. Very quiet.

There is nothing to see in the foyer, but in the living room….

Logic tells you that these must once have been several men; you can even recognize scraps of Knight Errant guard uniform scattered among the bits. The carnage is frightening. In your years on the streets and in the shadows, you have rarely seen mutilation as horrifying. You hope to God that whatever did it wasn't Human.

BEHIND THE SCENES

Euphoria has been kidnapped by Craft, a Flesh Form Worker, and several True Form Soldiers. After her release on Monday, Euphoria and Carrone met with Vincent Burroughs at his office in an attempt to connive some money from Burroughs even though Euphoria missed her appearances. They failed. A clause in Euphoria's contract guaranteed that he could withhold payment if she did not fulfill her schedule.

Tuesday morning, Burroughs heard through a corporate spy that Ludivenko was signing a deal with MegaMedia for Euphoria to do a promotion for Blue Bacosoy. Burroughs immediately contacted Craft and told him to get rid of Euphoria before she did the Ludivenko promotions. Burroughs wanted to give Ludivenko a taste of their own medicine. Craft, lost in his own fantasies, saw the opportunity to make a Queen and agreed to take care of Euphoria.

Tuesday evening, as soon as dark fell, several Soldiers carried Craft and a Worker up the outsidase wall of the Pacific Towers. One of the Soldiers ripped through the greenhouse balcony, and they entered the condo. Acting quickly, the Soldiers moved in on the surprised Knight Errant guards. The battle was short. Euphoria fainted in the midst of the carnage. The Soldiers then carried Craft and Euphoria out.

The runners might find several bits of valuable evidence at the penthouse. The clues are listed by area. Refer to the map of Euphoria's condo in **To Catch a Star**, p. 17.

The most important clue is in the recording studio. When the attack occurred, Euphoria was practicing lines for upcoming scenes of *Jungle Huntress*. Because she was using her wireless Sense Link, Craft did not realize that the abduction was being recorded. Most of the action is still intact on Euphoria's sim-sense equipment in the studio.

SCENE OF THE CRIME

Entrance Hall (1)

An abandoned guard station is here. A chair sits next to the door and a cup of cold soykaf that the front guard had been drinking remains on the floor. The main door is open.

Living Room (3)

Most of the action took place here. The doors to the foyer, recording studio, and balcony are all open. At the entrance to the foyer, there is a large, dark red stain on the carpet. By the stain are shreds of a Knight Errant uniform and a HK227 with a full clip. Here is where the front entrance guard met his end. There is much blood as well as some other remains.

The remains of two other guards lie scattered about the living room. Close examination by a knowledgeable character will reveal that all the wounds were caused by shredding or tearing. None are gunshot or sharp blade wounds. Whoever did the killing was also incredibly strong.

The glass doors to the balcony are shattered, and the wind whistles through the hole in the balcony's exterior. A Perception (8) Test will allow a character to notice some large holes in the ceiling, which make a path from the balcony doors to directly above the bloodstain near the foyer entrance.

A Perception (5) Test will also allow a character to notice a small lump of brown slime on the carpet near the couch. The Worker that came with the kidnapping group drooled some raw hive food onto the floor. If a character has tasted Amber Gel before, he may be able to recognize the smell or taste of the substance. This requires a Perception (6) Test for smell and (4) for taste. If successful, the character may be able to form a vague association between the slime and Amber Gel.

Recording Studio (4)

Euphoria's recording gear is still turned on. To replay the recording requires an Electronics (3) Test or an Intelligence (9) Test, as the equipment is rather complicated. Simsense headsets hang on the wall, or characters with datajacks can plug into the recorder directly through a cable. When the recording is replayed, see **Private Screening** below.

Greenhouse Balcony (5)

This area is very chilly because of a large hole in the greenhouse's clear plastic shell. The only thing here are the grisly remains of the entrance guard's body, which are hidden by tropical plants.

PRIVATE SCREENING

GAMEMASTER'S NOTE: The recording the character is about to experience is powerful. The recording was made at full sensitivity, with all normal inhibitors and filters removed. Being only one generation removed from the actual recording and played back on the same superb professional equipment used to record it makes its intensity almost overwhelming. The raw emotions are more powerful than a BTL chip.

The player whose character is experiencing the recording should interrupt the gamemaster if he wishes to stop the recording by turning the equipment off, jacking out, or ripping the headset off.

Read the following.

The headset is in place. It takes a little adjusting, having been tailored for someone else's head. It feels comfortable. Confident, you reach down to touch the keypad on the remote contr—

The world pitches to black and for a moment, you hang in a senseless limbo. Dark nothingness surrounds you. Nothing to touch, nothing to hear, nothing to feel. It shifts again and the world returns.

You feel the soft touch of her silk clothing against your body, the texture of the deep, rich carpet beneath your feet. You move toward one of the consoles in the empty room and she adjusts some settings, carefully setting the system for her own experienced, conditioned psyche.

You turn to the right and she presses some keys, bringing the rehearsal script onto a nearby prompting screen. The scene is hard and cruel. The Jungle Huntress has just returned to her village to find her family and friends massacred. She sighs. She doesn't like the story; violence bothers her. An uneasy familiarity slowly rises to the surface. She presses more buttons and a series of images appear on another monitor. News photos. War. Famine. Disease. Hunger. Poverty. You stare at them and her sorrow washes over you.

Such pain, inflicted on people by other people. The Princess's tribe massacred as the corporate helicopters fire volley after endless volley of napalm rockets into the village. The faces of children as the poisoned flood waters rise in Bangladesh. A thousand racists riot in Chicago, and an old woman is crushed underfoot. A young man holds his dead bride on the steps of a church, her blood staining his clothes. Horror. Sadness. Pain. Ang—

A loud crash shatters her concentration, throwing her control into fragments of emotion rapidly spinning away. Her senses are sharp, her emotions wild. The lights in the recording studio are bright, the sounds from without, in the living room, are loud.

You move quickly across the room and reach the door in only a few steps. Grasping it, you rap your hand around the door edge and feel something warm, no hot, and sticky on the far side. Carefully, you pull open the door and peer into the living room.

Beyond you is near darkness. Shapes and blurs dance in the room. The odor of blood, the stench of something else. A sound as flesh is torn from flesh and the scream of something human. Then, the clicking laughter of something that is not.

Your eyes slowly adjust to the dark as a shape rises in front of you. A thick liquid drips from the ends of its arms where there should be hands, but aren't. A sickly sweet, almost familiar smell assaults you. It's going to come for you. It's going to kill you. You are going to die.

Another shape steps into view and than another behind it. Both are partially caught in the subdued light of the recording studio. The first smiles at you. You can smell him. His stench is harsh to your senses. Long, unkempt blond hair flows around his face. Were he younger, cleaner, you might consider him handsome. The figure behind him is also a man, but he stands still and quiet. Short black hair, dirty, torn jeans, and a white shirt that reads "Garrety's Bar And Grill." He stares at you. There is something wrong with his eyes.

"Ah, Euphoria, never lovelier," the closer man says. The same sickly sweet odor is on his breath. "Don't be afraid. Everything will be all right." He cocks his head to one side and laughs almost to himself. "Now isn't that a silly thing to say? 'Don't be afraid, everything will be all right.' Be afraid. Things are far from right."

He laughs again and reaches out to seize your arms. "Burroughs said to take care of you. I will. I'll make you my Queen."

Without warning, a figure to your left stands. His left arm is gone, but in his right hand is the gleaming shape of a submachine gun. He screams as a thin beam of red light lances out from the top of the gun and centers on the laughing man's forehead. His body spasms as a dark shape drops down onto him from above, smashing him into the ground. A misshapen arm hidden within the folds of a long coat rises, falls, and then rises again, something coming free with it. It sprays dark, hot droplets across the wall, against your face.

Euphoria collapses. The world returns to darkness.

When the characters play back the recording of the abduction, they may get more than they bargained for. Euphoria's simsense equipment has been modified to cut the inhibitors and filters, something like a "Better Than Life" chip player. The character or characters who choose to relive the recording will suffer the same mental stress that Euphoria experienced during the abduction. The gamemaster should encourage the character who experiences the playback to roleplay the effects of those sensations. Remember, he is experiencing Euphoria's raw, unfiltered, even somewhat amplified, reaction to the events.

Anyone watching the character reliving the abduction will see him physically reenact the events on the recording. He will slowly move through the recording studio and out into the living room as his body automatically, crudely, reacts to the sensations being fed it.

The simsense machinery can be modified to reinstall the inhibitors. It requires an Electronics B/R (4) Test and a base time of four hours, assuming that the proper tools are available. With the inhibitors reinstalled, the recording will cause no undue stress to its users. Note that the recording is stored in Euphoria's machine and may not be removed and played on another machine unless it is copied to a regular simsense chip or master chip. Copying the recording requires an Electronics (5) Test, with a base time of 30 minutes. Euphoria has spare chips that the characters can use.

The characters are free to ask Carrone any questions they wish. He will answer them to the best of his ability without disclosing information damaging to MegaMedia. He will recognize the name Burroughs as belonging to an executive of Strice Foods, but he doesn't know very much about him. Carrone had

met Burroughs a few times to organize Euphoria's Amber Gel appearances and can give the runners directions to Burroughs' office (tenth floor of Soykyo Office Plaza). Carrone does not recognize Craft if the characters ask him to identify the man from the recording.

When the characters are finished searching the penthouse and questioning Carrone, they have several options. Any attempt to magically locate Euphoria will fail. By now, she is possessed by the Queen Ant Spirit, her Astral Form shrouded by the Queen. The characters are free to check their contacts for information. Consult the **Legwork** section, p. 56. If a decker goes exploring in Strice Foods' computer system, go to **Hacking Strice**, p. 34. If the players decide to check on Garrety's Bar and Grill after viewing the recording, go to **Missing Persons**, p. 35. When the characters are ready to talk to Burroughs, go to **Hey, Vince!**, p. 36.

DEBUGGING

The only serious problem here might come up if the characters miss the simsense recording. They may still talk to Burroughs, but it will be difficult to get much out of him without the evidence in the recording. If they miss the recording, let the characters go on about their search, with Carrone contacting them later to say that he found the recording and thinks they should experience it.

HACKING STRICE

BEHIND THE SCENES

If the characters choose to investigate Strice Foods' computer system, they will have to find its unlisted number, as per the **Shadowrun** rules, unless they can discover the system's access number from a contact. The latter requires an Etiquette (Street) (8), Etiquette (Corporate) (6), or Etiquette (Matrix) (5) Test. The computer system does not contain any vital clues, but raiding the system could prove to be financially profitable. If the characters are getting stuck in their search, the gamemaster can include more information in the system. These extra clues could involve anything from a rent payment for Craft's talismonger shop, which gives the shop's name and address, or a memo from a meeting between Burroughs and Craft.

If an external alert is sounded, the system will automatically enter complete shutdown within two minutes. The results of any Trace are sent to a printer at Burroughs' terminal and printed out automatically. If the decker is operating during the day, Burroughs will be in his office and will contact Lone Star with the results of the Trace. Otherwise, Burroughs will not find the printout till morning, when he will contact Lone Star.

STRICE FOODS SYSTEM MAP

The Strice computer system is a low-cost system and contains few of the "wiz-bang" graphics and icons that more illustrious corporations pay to decorate their systems.

SAN (Number 2206 (312-1752), Red-5, Access 5): Appears as a huge crystal wall and gate bearing the logo of Strice Foods.

SPU-1 (Orange-3, Trace and Dump 3): Appears as a simple polygon shape with the Trace and Dump program appearing as a shifting ball of light.

SPU-2 (Orange-3, Killer 4): Appears again as a simple polygon. The Killer IC, if it materializes, will take the form of a sparkling diamond of orange energy.

I/OP 1 (Green-3, Access 3): Appears as a white pyramid pulsing with energy. This is Burroughs' terminal at his office on the tenth floor of Soykyo Office Plaza.

I/OP 2 (Green-2, Access 2): A grouping of I/O systems representing the various desktop terminals in a variety of departments. They all appear as the standard orange pyramid icon.

SM (Orange-4, Blaster 3): Appears as a large truck with the Strice logo on its side. The slave module is linked to the autopiloted trucks that service the various production plants, including the Amber Gel facility. The trucks cannot be controlled from the slave module. Its only function is to warn the company if an autopilot program in a truck gets stuck. Someone must then go out and free the truck from its jam. The address of the Amber Gel facility in the Puyallup Barrens is also found here. The Blaster IC will appear as a small turret on the top of the truck.

CPU (Orange-4, Barrier 3, Tar Pit 4): Appears as an octagonal room with shimmering walls. The Barrier is a field of blue energy around the outside perimeter of the octagonal room. When a decker activates a utility, the Tar Pit appears as a large mouth that will swallow the utility, lick its lips, belch, and then spit back along the decker's path to poison all copies of the utility.

DS-1 (Orange-3, Barrier 4): Appears as a maze of twisting corridors whose walls blaze with stored data. The Barrier appears as a shimmering field at the maze's entrance. Purchase orders are recorded in this node. A decker can learn that the only products delivered to the Amber Gel production plant are jars, blue coloring agent, and preprocessed, low-grade nutrisoy. How a stuffer can be made from only those ingredients should be mystifying. A decker can also learn that MegaMedia was to be paid 1,280,000 nuyen for Euphoria's three appearances. There are also files showing expenditures for Knight Errant Security, MegaMedia's production of the five-minute promotional sim, and rental of facilities for the appearances. The four valuable files here are 70 Mp each. They are worth a total of 28,000 nuyen before fencing.

DS-2 (Orange-5, Scramble 3): Appears as a large library with many tunnels and small rooms. The "books" on the library shelves store data. The Scramble will light up at the library's exit and whine its warning, as normal. Accounts Receivable are stored in this datastore. There are three files of 80 Mp each, which are worth a total of 60,000 nuyen. The street price will be less.

DS-3 (Green-3): Appears as a single rectangular room. A list of Strice Foods retailers and distributors in the Seattle area is kept here. There are two files of 40 Mp each. They are worth a total of 4,000 nuyen before fencing.

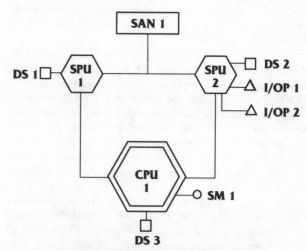

STRICE COMPUTER SYSTEM

MISSING PERSONS

TELL IT TO THEM STRAIGHT

Garrety's Bar and Grill is situated near enough to the real action places to have a glimmer of street edge to it, but it's far enough removed to be safe from the true street crowd. It's the kind of place where corp types like to go slumming, because it has the aura of a street bar but is actually pretty safe. Someone who has really tasted the action would find Garrety's a pale imitation.

The place has a bar, a dance floor, and some tables and booths. In one corner are various credstick-operated sim machines and arcade games. You notice a waitress wearing a Garrety's Bar and Grill T-shirt like the one you saw in the sim. Several other waitresses and waiters, all wearing the same T-shirts, are serving customers at the tables. A big, beefy man stands behind the bar talking with some customers.

BEHIND THE SCENES

If the players decide to investigate the T-shirt clue from the sim recording, they will wind up at Garrety's Bar and Grill, a restaurant and pub located in downtown Seattle. (The runners can get the pub's address from any local directory.) Garrety's serves a basic line of grilled food and keeps a well-stocked bar. Its clientele is mostly lower-level sararimen and other middle class people.

The man behind the bar is the pub's owner and chief bartender, Bill Garrety. (Use **Bartender** Contact p. 163, **SR** rules.) Three waitresses and one waiter are on duty. (Use **Pedestrian** Contact, p. 116, **Sprawl Sites**.) At night, a Troll Bouncer is also on duty (p. 173, **SR** rules).

The Worker shown in Euphoria's simsense recording is a former Garrety's waiter named Van Willis. He was kidnapped from the bar almost a month ago while out back emptying trash in a dumpster. Garrety happened to witness Willis being dragged through a manhole into the sewers, but he has not, and will not, say a word to anyone. Garrety is not especially brave, and he's heard some disturbing rumors about the recent spate of disappearances in the area. He figures some poor sap who waited tables at Garrety's pub isn't worth getting on the bad side of some fanatic cult.

If the characters start asking questions about missing waiters, Garrety will pretend ignorance. He will admit only that Van Willis, who used to work for him and who disappeared about a month ago, fits the rough description they give.

Two of the waitresses on duty knew Willis. One will do no more than confirm that Willis inexplicably disappeared about a month ago. The other waitress, Wendy Phillips, will tell the characters more if they speak with her when Garrety is not nearby. If the characters do not talk with her before they leave the bar, she will catch them as they leave. "Hey, were you asking about Van Willis?" Wendy asks, then goes on to give the characters the following story.

"I knew Van pretty well because we had the same shift. He was a nice kid, though a little on the slow side. He wouldn't get a gold medal in the mental Olympics, if you know what I mean. Anyway, he disappeared about a month ago. I think Garrety knows more than he'll admit, but I don't blame him for not talking. There's been a lot of talk on the street about some cult that's been kidnapping street people, and I think the same people got Willis. At first I thought it was a hoax like that barghest scare last year, but then I saw Willis about two weeks ago. It was late and the streetlights were out on the street, but I recognized him from a distance. When I started toward him and called his name, he just looked at me and ran away. I got a better look at him, though, and he had changed. I'm sure it was him, but with something like scars all over his face. I got scared and ran away myself."

Wendy does not recall exactly where she saw Willis, claiming she was intoxicated and had gotten off at the wrong rail stop in a strange part of town. The only thing she remembers is that Willis was standing in front of a shop named "Magic Crafts." This is Dorin's old magic shop, though Wendy does not know that. She thinks Willis's scars were from some kind of initiation to the cult that took him. In reality, those "scars" are sections of chitin covering Willis' skin.

DEBUGGING

If the runners are stupid enough to start a bar brawl at Garrety's, let them get beaten senseless just for the heck of it. They deserve it.

TELL IT TO THEM STRAIGHT

She stares at you, her expression even more vacant than a moment before. "You want to see whom?"

She snorts with laughter, as though your request were the funniest thing she'd ever heard.

BEHIND THE SCENES

The characters will eventually have to talk to Vincent Burroughs, the Strice Foods exec in charge of Amber Gel. Vincent's office is on the tenth floor of the Soykyo Office Plaza building in downtown Seattle. Strice Foods has all its Seattle central offices on the tenth and eleventh floors of the building.

Being able to get in to see Burroughs at his office will require some finesse and fast-talking savvy. If the runners try to come into a crowded office building with guns blazing, a large force from Lone Star will show up immediately to haul them off to detention. The characters will have to make a series of Etiquette (Corporate) Skill Tests to get to see Burroughs. The gamemaster should modify the Target Numbers for these tests according to the quality of roleplaying leading up to the test. The general appearance of the player characters can also modify the test. A group in business suits may get a –1 to Target Numbers, whereas a group in street clothes armed with assault rifles will probably get a +4 to Target Numbers, plus a call to Lone Star or building security. If more than one character wants to use his Etiquette Skill, the Target Number for each test increases by +2 for every individual past the first attempting each test.

When the characters enter the eleventh floor, they will first have to deal with the receptionist on duty. (Use **Corporate Secretary** Contact, p. 165, **SR** rules.) She is pleasant to visitors, but getting through her requires an Etiquette (Corporate) (5) Test.

---

0 Success	"I'm sorry, but Mr. Burroughs is tied up in meetings the rest of the day. Try again, or phone ahead for an appointment next time. Honestly!"
1-2 Successes	"Yes, Mr. Burroughs' secretary will see you now to set up an appointment. However, I believe Mr. Burroughs is busy right now."
3+ Successes	"Well, if you're expected…Of course. Down the hall and take your second right."

Once the characters have made it through to Burroughs' private secretary, (p. 165, **SR** rules), they must make another Etiquette (Corporate) (6) Test. The test determines how soon they can get an appointment to see Burroughs. The base time is eight hours divided by the number of successes they achieved on their test. It is possible that a result may carry the appointment over to the next business day. Four or more successes will get them an immediate appointment.

When the characters finally get to meet with Burroughs, his secretary ushers them into his office. Occupying a corner of the building, Burroughs' office has two views of the city. It also has plush furniture, a well-stocked bar, and a huge desk with computer terminal and printer. The desk terminal accesses the computer system, as described in **Hacking Strice**, p. 34.

When the characters meet Burroughs, he is on the verge of a nervous breakdown. Craft contacted him a few days ago to inform him that the production of Amber Gel had halted indefinitely. Burroughs does not know why production has stopped, only that the plant is no longer producing. (The reason for the halt in production is that the Queen Spirit has commanded Craft to concentrate the Hive on creating and maintaining her cocoon.)

Unable to contact Craft, Burroughs has ordered his security chief, Henry Killian, to take some men into the forbidden sections of the production plant (where the secret Hive resides) to try to discover why production has stopped and where Craft is. Burroughs is already under tremendous pressure from higher management to increase Amber Gel production, and if his superiors discover that production has halted completely, Burroughs will certainly be demoted and replaced.

Unfortunately for Burroughs, things are only going to get worse for him. When Killian took his men into the facility, Ant Soldiers massacred them. Angry at Burroughs, Craft has dispatched a True Form Soldier (Force 3) to kill him.

Burroughs will invite the runners to have a seat, taking them at face value about the business matter they have invented to get in here. He is casual and pleasant until the player characters begin to probe into either Euphoria's whereabouts or the secrets of Amber Gel. He will pretend ignorance of Euphoria's second disappearance. "Really? I hadn't heard it in the news. Are you sure?" He will also lead the conversation away from talk of Amber Gel. "Yes, we've got quite a product. How about those Timberwolves? You keep up with the combat bike teams?"

If the player characters drop all pretenses, Burroughs becomes very serious, too. The team will have to pressure Burroughs to get any real information out of him. One character must make an Etiquette (Corporate), Interrogation, or Negotiation (6) Test. If the characters blackmail Burroughs with a copy of Euphoria's abduction recording, apply a –2 modifier to the Target Number of their Skill Test.

0 Success	"Look, you've got nothing on me. And if you're not out of here in two seconds, I'll have you arrested."
1 Success	"All right, look, I've got an outside business partner for Amber Gel. He handles all the production and everything. I'm just a front. I don't know anything. The guy calls himself Craft. That's all I know."
2+ Successes	"O.K., take it easy. I'll tell you what I know. This guy named Craft came to see me with this new product. It tasted great so I surveyed and taste-tested it. We came to a preliminary agreement and then he showed me how it was produced. Like honey. But…but, I went ahead with the product anyway. Craft handled all production and everything. I'm just a front. "And then this deal with Euphoria came up, but Ludivenko hired some dirtbags to lift her so she would miss the promotions. After that, I find out through sources that Ludivenko's going to use Euphoria to promote their Amber Gel clone—something called Blue Bacosoy. I tell Craft we can't let that happen. So, he goes and takes Euphoria and says he going to make her into his…."

As the characters are breaking Burroughs down, a shimmering suddenly appears in the air, then the Ant Spirit materializes and immediately attacks Burroughs, obviously intending to kill him.

The runners may be able to prevent this. At the very last moment, have them make a Perception (9) Test.

0 Success	The character is completely surprised. Follow normal surprise procedures, per **Perception and Reality**, p. 156, **SR** rules.
1 – 3 Successes	The Spirit gets an attack, but the player character can act normally next action.
4 Successes	Character gets one action as the Spirit attacks. Resolve the character's action first.
5+ Successes	Roll for Initiative between the Spirit and the character resolving a normal initiative turn. No one else may act. If another character scored 4 successes, he may act on the Spirit's first action.

The Spirit's first priority is to kill Burroughs. It is not at all concerned about the player characters. Once Burroughs is dead, the Spirit flees.

If the runners can keep Burroughs alive, he'll tell all. If they can't, his secretary will tell them everything she knows.

WHAT BURROUGHS KNOWS

Very little, actually. He can tell the runners that a man named Craft approached him a few months ago, claiming to have a food product that would make Strice Foods king of the industry. Burroughs was skeptical, but a taste of the prototype gel that Craft presented was enough to convince him. The problem was that Craft insisted on complete secrecy about his source. Burroughs was desperate. During his term as head of the Modern Masterpieces division, sales of the line had been slow. Word had come down that unless sales showed a marked upswing real soon, Burroughs' position with the corp was in doubt.

Burroughs decided to make a deal with Craft, supplied him with the additional raw materials needed to make Amber Gel, and sat back to watch as his value in the company rose. No one upstairs even bothered to check on where Amber Gel was produced. They didn't care. It made money. Lots of money.

That was then. A few days ago, Craft informed Burroughs that production of Amber Gel had, for reasons beyond his control, halted. He promised that production would resume shortly, but Burroughs has not heard from Craft since.

Earlier that day, Burroughs ordered Strice Security Director Killian and a group of guards to find out what was going on at the Amber Gel production facility.

Burroughs can give them the address of the Amber Gel facility, south of Puyallup, off Pioneer Highway. He will even offer them a flat 10,000 nuyen if they can learn what has happened to production of the stuffer.

WHAT THE SECRETARY KNOWS

Not a lot. She knows little about the deal with Craft, but does know the address of the production facility in Puyallup and the one Craft gave for his royalty/paychecks. The latter address is in the Redmond Barrens, near St. James Lake.

If the Spirit succeeds in killing Burroughs, the secretary will also be able to clear the runners of any blame for his death.

NEXT STOP

If the runners intend to visit Craft's address in the Redmond Barrens, go to **The Magic Shop**, the next section. If they go to the Amber Gel facility, go to **Audience With The Queen**, p. 43.

DEBUGGING

This section assumes that the characters are attempting to meet Burroughs at his office. If they are somehow able to get a picture I.D. of Burroughs or to see him over a vidphone, they can try to spot him coming out of the Soykyo building and tail him to his home. Shadowing him will require an automobile. The driver must get at least two successes in both the appropriate Vehicle Skill Test at Target Number 4 and in a Stealth Test at Target Number 5. If both rolls get no more than two successes, the driver either loses Burroughs in rush-hour traffic or is spotted by him, depending on which roll failed. Burroughs lives in a nice condominium with light security. If the characters corner him there, handle the discussion just as though they were at his office. The Spirit will still arrive and try to kill Burroughs. Unfortunately, the secretary won't be there to provide information or to clear the runners if the Soldier is successful.

To get to the end of the adventure, the characters need to discover the name Craft. If they fail to get it from Burroughs, they must discover it either by decking the Amber Gel computer system or by finding it on Burroughs' desk. If the characters get arrested, they were stupid and probably deserve to languish in jail, but let them out on bail so they can finish the mission.

OTHER NPCS

BURROUGHS

Burroughs is an obese man of 51 years, who favors pin-stripe suits and lots of jewelry. His face is free of cosmetic surgery, though it could use some, and his gray hair is always neatly combed and conservatively styled.

B	Q	S	C	I	W	E	M	R	Armor
3	2	2	4	4	2	4.8	—	3	None

Dice Pools: Defense (Armed) 1, Defense (Unarmed) 1, Dodge 3
Skills: Computer Theory 3, Etiquette (Corporate) 4, Interrogation 3, Negotiation 4
Cyberware: Datajack, 100Mp of memory
Gear: None

TRUE FORM SOLDIER (FORCE 3)

B	Q	S	C	I	W	E	M	R	Armor
4	7	7	—	1	2	(3)A	—	6 (11)	3/3

Attacks: 7M2 Physical plus Special
Powers: Enhanced Senses (Smell), Manifestation, Paralyzing Touch, Venom
Weaknesses: Reduced Senses (Sight), Vulnerability (Insecticides)

THE MAGIC SHOP

TELL IT TO THEM STRAIGHT

As the sun sets on another smog-filled day, you walk a desolate street in search of this man called Craft. You silently thank your contacts as you come closer to the building. A dozen meters away you see the vague shape of someone standing in the shadow of the doorway.

GAMEMASTER'S NOTE: If anyone attempts to inspect the shop astrally, read the following:

The street is cold and etched with the misery of those who live on it. You glide slowly toward your destination, but then notice a pale luminescence coming from the store's doorway. Keeping yourself hidden, you make out a human figure standing there, but its aura is alien, inhuman. In fact, it's a huge ant.

BEHIND THE SCENES

Standing guard in the doorway is Van Willis, the former waiter at Garrety's Bar and Grill, now possessed by a Worker Ant Spirit and accompanying Craft as a guard. He is three weeks into his Possession and his form has begun to alter. He wears heavy, bulky clothing to conceal the change, but it is impossible to hide it from anyone up close. If the runners get near enough, they will see that Willis is wearing the same tattered and torn T-shirt with the "Garrety's" logo that he had on when kidnapped three weeks ago.

Craft has not been in the store for nearly a month, but some clues still exist and some hints about Craft's personality.

DEBUGGING

The runners' visit to the magic shop is intended as a source of clues and hints, not as an early demise. Neither Van Willis nor the attack Ant Spirits that show up should be too much for the player characters to handle. The encounter with the Ant Spirits should be an instructional encounter rather than a final one. Combat with a Spirit of any kind is different from what the runners are used to thus far. See **Insects Among Us**, p. 54.

VAN WILLIS (FLESH FORM WORKER, FORCE 1)

Craft has left Willis here primarily as a scare tactic, because the Worker Spirit cannot fight. He does know how to look mean, though. He just stands there.

B	Q	S	C	I	W	E	M	R	Armor
2	2	2	—	1	1	(1)A	—	1	None

Attacks: None
Powers: Enhanced Senses (Smell)
Weaknesses: Reduced Senses (Sight)

CONDITION MONITOR

PHYSICAL	MENTAL
Unconscious.> Possibly dead	< Unconscious. Further damage causes wounds.
Seriously > Wounded.	< Seriously Fatigued.
Moderately > Wounded.	< Moderately Fatigued.
Lightly > Wounded.	< Lightly Fatigued.

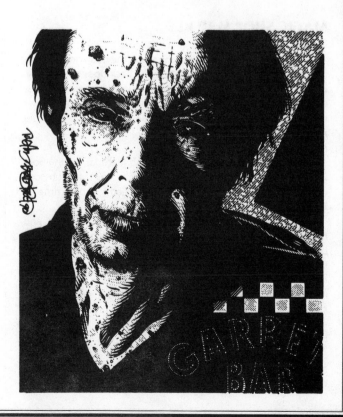

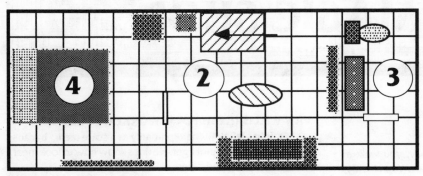

Lower Level

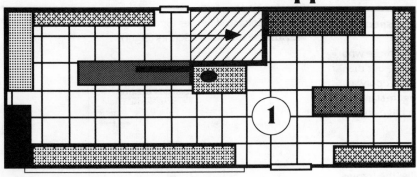

Upper Level

CRAFT'S MAGIC
SHOP

☐ = 1 meter

MAGIC SHOP MAP KEY

There are two entrances to the store, the main door, where the former Van Willis is standing, and a back door to the alley. Both the front and alley doors are closed and locked. The alley door lock is in better condition than the front and shows evidence of having been recently used. Both have a Barrier Rating of 5.

Main Store Area (1)

All that remains here is some fetish material worth about 2,500 nuyen to anyone interested in such things. It is obvious on first sight that the store hasn't been used for some time.

Downstairs/Living Area (2)

Craft lived downstairs until the coming of the Hive, and now maintains it as a private escape where he can be Human for brief periods. In the main living area, which shows signs of use in the past week, the runners find a variety of electronic entertainment gear, including trideo, LiveSound audio equipment, and a simsense player and some chips. If examined, the chips turn out to be mainly Euphoria sims. A crude map of the Amber Gel production facility, including its location, is also here.

The remains of various foodstuffs are around: normal microwave fixings, stuffers, and copious empty Amber Gel containers lie in and around the kitchenette area.

The stench here is strong, and anyone who knows the odor will recognize it as dried blood.

Downstairs/Bathroom (3)

As malodorous as the worst semi-abandoned transient hotel where any of the runners have lived, this room apparently has not been cleaned in months. As soon as the lights come on, hundreds of roaches scurry quickly into hiding.

Downstairs/Bedroom (4)

This room is the source of the stench. A rather decadent bedroom, it shows obvious signs of having been used for other purposes. The walls are covered with two- and three-dimensional photos and illustrations of Euphoria, many of them blood-splattered. Judging solely by the amount of blood stains everywhere, it is apparent that at least one person, possibly more, has been killed here.

A search of the room reveals some trideo and simsense records units, but no tapes or chips. In the closet, the runners discover facsimiles of clothing worn by Euphoria in various sims. They also find a collection of wigs and hairpieces similar to the hair style made fashionable by Euphoria.

Craft has an unhealthy fascination with Euphoria. Over the years, he has lured a number of women here, mostly prostitutes, dressed them as the star and then acted out his fantasies. The most recent occurrence was about a week ago before he actually kidnapped Euphoria.

A MEGAMEDIA PRODUCTION

TELL IT TO THEM STRAIGHT

Carrone's been badgering you for a report, and now he's got it. Surprisingly, he doesn't question your sanity, but instead leans back reflectively. "It's obvious," he says finally, "that the center of all this is the production facility. I think we go in."

Your arguments notwithstanding, he insists. "This is, of course, outside the bounds of your original contract. We'll make this a legally correct, official corporate action, that sort of thing, and outfit you completely. I'm authorized to offer each of you 75,000 nuyen for your participation in the rescue of Euphoria."

BEHIND THE SCENES

In case no one has noticed, *MegaMedia* wants Euphoria back *bad*. After Brighton's defection to Brilliant Genesis, MegaMedia cannot afford to lose another big star. The silver lining for Carrone is that he intends to record Euphoria's rescue.

Following the Negotiation for the final payment per runner, Carrone has the runners sign the contract found in the **Player Handouts** section. If a runner refuses to sign, he will not be able to participate in the run. Non-negotiable issue.

Following this, all will be transported to a small warehouse near the Tacoma docks. Here they meet Warden, an Elven Armorer of some repute. If a runner makes a successful Etiquette (Street) 3 Test, he knows about Warden. The Elf's reputation is that if you want it and can pay for it, he can get it.

He smiles at the player characters, then says, "Going hunting, I hear. What you need?" One of the player characters will no doubt ask for some outlandish piece of hardware. Give it to him or her. That should make someone stop and think.

The runners should be as heavily armed as possible for the fight in the Hive. Within the following guidelines, no weapon should be off-limits:

·Keep careful track of the total weight carried by each character, per **Hauling The Load**, p. 156, **SR** rules.

·Among all the weapons in the **Shadowrun** rulebook, only the Medium and Heavy Machine Guns will not be available. If the player characters choose, they can also get Harley Scorpion motorcycles.

·From the **Street Samurai Catalog**, only the MP-Laser, the FN Medium and M107 Heavy Machine Guns are not available. If the runners wish, they can get Honda Viking motorcycles. (Yes, they can have a Minigun mounted on a Deluxe Gyro-Mount if they wish.)

·Communication gear will be available, but will be installed in the Security Armor that MegaMedia provides.

The following equipment breakdown is recommended, but the runners may add, subtract, or augment as they wish.

(1) Set of Medium Security Armor with Security Helmet (combined Armor Rating of 7/7) with the following options:

> Heads-Up Data Display
> Low-Light Amplification
> Signal Locator
> Smartgun Link (equivalent of Smart Goggles)
> Thermographic
> Tracking Signal (4)
> Transceiver (Helmet)

(2) IPE Airfoil Offensive Grenades (5S4)

(2) IPE Standard Defensive Grenades (5S4)

(1) Primary Weapon of Choice, Rifle or larger. Will be provided in Smart version with applicable recoil reduction, APDS, or Explosive Ammo, as requested, Mini-Grenade Launcher, Rangefinder, Rangefinder-Grenade Link (Airburst), and 6 IPE Mini-Grenades, as requested, and sufficient ammo for said weapons.

(1) Secondary Weapon of Choice, Rifle or smaller. As above, but must be a lighter weapon than the primary choice.

(1) Back-up Weapon of Choice, Heavy Pistol or smaller. As above, but must be a lighter weapon than the secondary choice.

(1) Stimulant Patch (6)

(1) Trauma Patch (6)

The fight with the Ant Hive will be violent and bloody, and the runners should be armed for it. Remember, however, that they will not get to keep the equipment they've been issued: they must return all of it at the end of the run.

Carrone tells them that he will be continually monitoring the runners' progress in the facility from the command truck outside and that he will authorize reinforcements if necessary. Because this is an official corporate action by MegaMedia, everything must be done by the book. Transportation from the warehouse to the facility is by means of a bonded transport vehicle, within which the runners are sealed for the duration of the trip. The drivers are not MegaMedia employees, but staff drivers for Russel Overland. If necessary, they can testify in court that they picked the runners up in one corporate territory, transported them across Seattle, and deposited them adjacent to the territory of another corporation and that no one ever left the vehicle.

What the runners do not know is that MegaMedia has hidden simsense recording gear in the armor they are wearing. In addition to the armor's built-in tracking and communications equipment, this hidden gear will record and transmit the events of the run. If nothing else, Carrone expects it to be a hell of a show.

Should one of the runners do a detailed examination of the suit, he will need a successful Electronics (B/R) (12) Test to recognize the simsense recording gear.

DEBUGGING

The only thing that could go wrong in this section is that the runners refuse the contract. If they do, a greater monetary inducement might change their minds. If they still refuse, so be it. Perhaps the team MegaMedia does send into the Hive will be victorious. If not, the Hive could come looking for our reluctant team of runners for some reason.

AUDIENCE WITH THE QUEEN

TELL IT TO THEM STRAIGHT

The command van deposits you within spitting distance of the Amber Gel facility. In the moonlight, nothing is visible within the compound. Nothing moves.

The building appears to be deserted, with no lights and no sign of activity. But wait, was that something moving on the roof?

BEHIND THE SCENES

As indicated on the Amber Gel Facility Map below, only two guards are outside the building. Both are Flesh Form Soldiers (Force 3). As the Queen is not yet completely summoned, a true hive-mind does not exist. At this time, these sentries can be killed without alerting the rest of the Hive. If given the opportunity, they will make a dash for the building's interior.

Inside, among the unused machinery, are two Flesh Form Workers (Force 1), whose sole instructions are to flee into the depths of the facility to alert Craft and the Hive if they spot intruders.

Either the elevator or the stairway will take the runners to the lower level of the facility, where the Hive has its residence. Shown on the map are the various Worker areas, the vats for mixing the Amber Gel with the Worker excretion, and the drums for transporting it to the packaging plant.

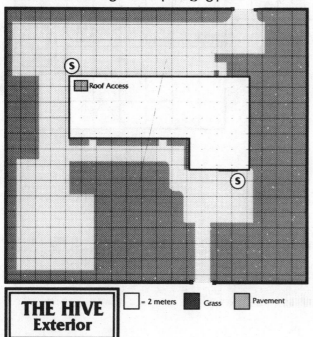

Roof Access

☐ = 2 meters   ▨ Grass   ▨ Pavement

THE HIVE
Exterior

AMBER GEL FACILITY MAP KEY

UPPER LEVEL

Main Area

This area is not much used by the Hive, and shows signs of only general activity. Trucks from Strice Foods are loaded up at the loading dock, but the only person the truckers occasionally see is Craft. When the truckers arrive each morning, the drums of Amber Gel are already waiting for them.

The rest of the area is taken up by equipment for conventional methods of food production. Upon examination, they prove to be dusty and poorly maintained.

The elevator is a conventional freight elevator that connects this level with the one below it. It is fully operational. The control panel shows some signs of physical damage but is usable.

In the far corner is a stairway that leads up to the roof and down to the next level. None of the access doors are locked, and the stairway is unlit.

The only light in the Upper Level is what filters in through the high, green-tinted windows along each wall. The power is on, so the runners could turn on the fluorescent overheads if they wished.

None of the doors leading into the building are locked and all are easily operable.

Offices

Near the stairway is a small group of offices. All are empty and abandoned.

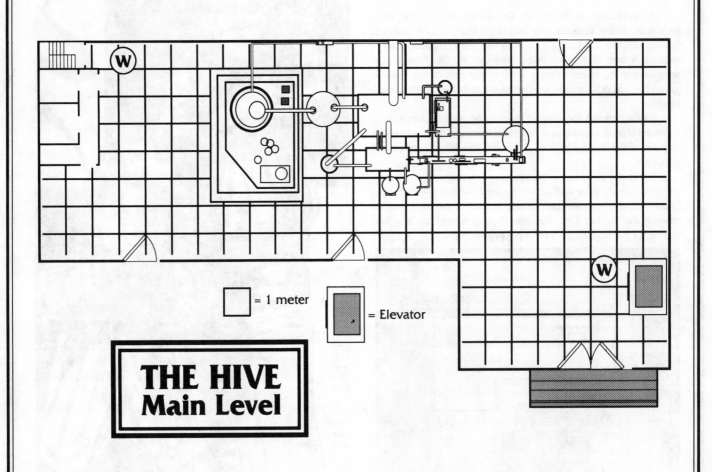

= 1 meter

= Elevator

THE HIVE Main Level

LOWER LEVEL

The Lower Level is dark, with neither light nor power for light. The air is stale and reeks of things sweet and pungent. If anyone happens to notice, there are not any normal insects or rodents found on this level.

Unless otherwise noted, all rooms are dirty and debris-filled. Some have piles of crates either full or waiting to be filled with basic soy foods, some unprocessed.

All the Lower Level walls are relatively weak, with a Barrier Rating of 3. If the Soldiers make an all-out attack, they will use the thin walls to their advantage.

Room 1

The elevator unloads into this room. Unless the Hive has been alerted, nothing will be found here.

Room 2

See **Room 1**.

Room 3

A Worker room. Six Flesh Form Workers (Force 1) are here, as are two Flesh Form Soldiers (Force 3).

Room 4 – 7

See **Room 1**.

Room 8

The stairway exits into this room. Two Flesh Form Workers (Force 1) are here.

Room 9 – 13

See **Room 1**.

Room 14

A Worker room. Four Flesh Form Workers (Force 1) and two Flesh Form Soldiers (Force 3) are here.

Room 15

A Worker room. Five Flesh Form Workers (Force 1) and a lone Flesh Form Soldier (Force 5) are here.

Room 16

The Hive Room. See below.

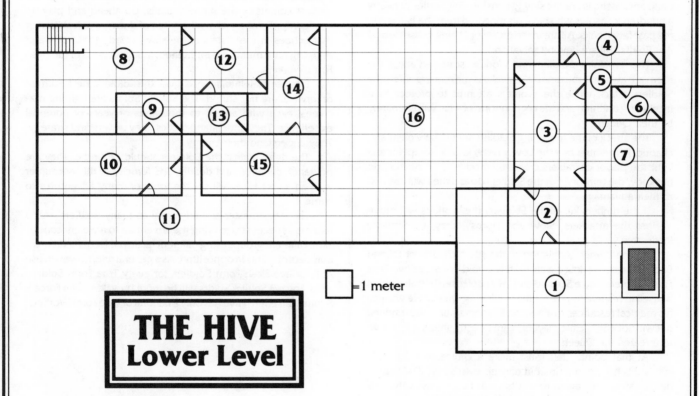

= 1 meter

THE HIVE
Lower Level

THE HIVE ROOM

When the runners enter the Hive Room, read them the following:

"The larger ones are fierce fighters. Pain does little to slow them down. To stop them, you have to kill them. The last round slams into one of the squealing things, sending another spray of blood across the wall. It jerks once and then lies still.

"As the empty clip drops from your gun, it clatters at your feet. By all rights, you should allow the barrel of your assault rifle to cool, but there's no time. You slap another magazine into the weapon and let the bolt fly forward, chambering another round. Your teammates are waiting and you move into the next room.

"A sight from your worst nightmares assails you. Dark, amber cocoons fill the room, and shadowy, human-shaped bodies writhe inside them. Immediately, dozens of the same half-human, half-something else rush at you. Beyond them stands a wild-haired man, the look in his eyes also wild with power. He laughs as giant, ant-shaped creatures manifest around him.

"They attack."

The room is filled with scores of cocoons. Within those dark, amber shells are the slowly transforming bodies of nearly a hundred lost souls who have disappeared from the Barrens in the past few weeks. All are in the process of being possessed by Ant Spirits. All are beyond salvation.

The remaining Soldiers and Workers scattered about the room are awaiting the runners' arrival. As the runners enter, the Soldiers attack while the Workers attempt to protect their incubating brethren and the cocoon-form of what will ultimately be their Queen.

The attack of the remaining Soldiers should be violent and chaotic. Remember that the Lower Level is dark except for any light the player characters create themselves. The runners do not know the territory, but the Soldiers do and they will use that to their advantage.

If the runners kill all the Soldiers, the Workers will move against the attackers. Slow and clumsy, they are virtually ineffective.

In one corner of this room, the giant cocoon of Queen Euphoria rests against a wall. Craft will hold in reserve two True Form Soldiers (Force 5) to aid him in her defense. Craft also holds himself in reserve to protect the incubating Queen. He will use his magical resources to assist the Soldiers against the runners, but will not engage the players' team directly unless they move to threaten the Queen.

At that point, Craft must make a choice. The Queen's survival is his first priority, but only his own survival will allow him to start over again if necessary. If he perceives that his chances of defeating the runners' attack are close to nothing, he will attempt to escape. But Craft will make this decision only if events force it on him as the only option.

The Ants, on the other hand, will fight to the death for their Queen. With her arrival so imminent, they have nothing to live for without her. They will continue to fight even if Craft escapes. Should they somehow overcome the runners, the Ants will go looking for Craft again. He is, after all, their shaman.

If the Queen is disrupted or banished and any True or Flesh Form Ant Spirits still exist, they will search out Craft to begin work on the new Hive.

ASTRAL SCOUTING

If the runners attempt to Astrally Scout the production facility, they will encounter a pair of True Form Soldiers (Force 5) who keep up their attack until the intruders withdraw. At that point, the Hive becomes aware that they are potentially under attack. Should the intruders persist, Craft begins to send pairs of True Form Soldiers after them. He also sends a pair of True Form Workers, hoping outsiders will not detect the difference between the aggressive Soldiers and the Workers, who do not fight.

If the fight begins to turn against the Hive, Craft will send out a True Form Soldier to scout the area. If he locates the runners, he will mass his remaining forces against them. He will remain behind at all times to protect the Queen, always maintaining Astral Perception.

DEBUGGING

The gamemaster is encouraged to use all the storytelling ability at his disposal as the runners begin their assault. Terror should lurk behind every corner, in the rafters above, and in the darkest corners of the runners' souls. Go ahead and play up tactile impressions such as the smell of decay, a soft skittering that echoes in the distance, the slow, steady tones of water dripping onto metal, the frightened, inhuman wails of the Flesh Form Workers.

Despite their intelligence level, the Soldiers, Flesh Form or otherwise, are not stupid. The Soldier Spirits are fighting machines, each with access to thousands of years of potential experience. They understand tactics, they understand strategy. They understand their enemy.

The fight against the Soldiers should be brutal. They are powerful, cunning, and deadly. The ferocity of this encounter with an Insect Hive will set the tone for many adventures to come.

The gamemaster should throw as many Soldiers at the runners as necessary to bring the adventure to a violent conclusion. Different groups using different tactics will require different numbers of Spirits in opposition. As a general rule, however, use at least five Flesh Form Soldiers for every True Form Soldier. Also, Force 3 Soldier Spirits will be more prevalent than Force 5 Spirits. The entire Hive has only a handful of True Form Workers.

FLESH FORM WORKER (FORCE 1)

B	Q	S	C	I	W	E	M	R	Armor
2	2	2	—	1	1	(1)A	—	1	None

Attacks: None

Powers: Enhanced Senses (Smell)

Weaknesses: Reduced Senses (Sight)

CONDITION MONITOR
PHYSICAL   **MENTAL**

Unconscious.> Possibly dead
< Unconscious. Further damage causes wounds.

Seriously > Wounded.
< Seriously Fatigued.

Moderately > Wounded.
< Moderately Fatigued.

Lightly > Wounded.
< Lightly Fatigued.

CONDITION MONITOR
PHYSICAL   **MENTAL**

Unconscious.> Possibly dead
< Unconscious. Further damage causes wounds.

Seriously > Wounded.
< Seriously Fatigued.

Moderately > Wounded.
< Moderately Fatigued.

Lightly > Wounded.
< Lightly Fatigued.

CONDITION MONITOR
PHYSICAL   **MENTAL**

Unconscious.> Possibly dead
< Unconscious. Further damage causes wounds.

Seriously > Wounded.
< Seriously Fatigued.

Moderately > Wounded.
< Moderately Fatigued.

Lightly > Wounded.
< Lightly Fatigued.

CONDITION MONITOR
PHYSICAL   **MENTAL**

Unconscious.> Possibly dead
< Unconscious. Further damage causes wounds.

Seriously > Wounded.
< Seriously Fatigued.

Moderately > Wounded.
< Moderately Fatigued.

Lightly > Wounded.
< Lightly Fatigued.

CONDITION MONITOR
PHYSICAL   **MENTAL**

Unconscious.> Possibly dead
< Unconscious. Further damage causes wounds.

Seriously > Wounded.
< Seriously Fatigued.

Moderately > Wounded.
< Moderately Fatigued.

Lightly > Wounded.
< Lightly Fatigued.

CONDITION MONITOR
PHYSICAL   **MENTAL**

Unconscious.> Possibly dead
< Unconscious. Further damage causes wounds.

Seriously > Wounded.
< Seriously Fatigued.

Moderately > Wounded.
< Moderately Fatigued.

Lightly > Wounded.
< Lightly Fatigued.

CONDITION MONITOR
PHYSICAL   **MENTAL**

Unconscious.> Possibly dead
< Unconscious. Further damage causes wounds.

Seriously > Wounded.
< Seriously Fatigued.

Moderately > Wounded.
< Moderately Fatigued.

Lightly > Wounded.
< Lightly Fatigued.

CONDITION MONITOR
PHYSICAL   **MENTAL**

Unconscious.> Possibly dead
< Unconscious. Further damage causes wounds.

Seriously > Wounded.
< Seriously Fatigued.

Moderately > Wounded.
< Moderately Fatigued.

Lightly > Wounded.
< Lightly Fatigued.

CONDITION MONITOR
PHYSICAL   **MENTAL**

Unconscious.> Possibly dead
< Unconscious. Further damage causes wounds.

Seriously > Wounded.
< Seriously Fatigued.

Moderately > Wounded.
< Moderately Fatigued.

Lightly > Wounded.
< Lightly Fatigued.

CONDITION MONITOR
PHYSICAL   **MENTAL**

Unconscious.> Possibly dead
< Unconscious. Further damage causes wounds.

Seriously > Wounded.
< Seriously Fatigued.

Moderately > Wounded.
< Moderately Fatigued.

Lightly > Wounded.
< Lightly Fatigued.

TRUE FORM WORKERS (FORCE 1)

B	Q	S	C	I	W	E	M	R	Armor
1	1	3	—	1	1	(1)A	—	3 (8)	None

Attacks: None

Powers: Enhanced Senses (Smell), Manifestation, Paralyzing Touch, Venom

Weaknesses: Reduced Senses (Sight), Vulnerability (Insecticides)

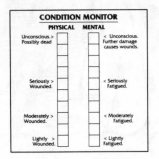

CONDITION MONITOR

PHYSICAL	MENTAL
Unconscious.> Possibly dead	< Unconscious. Further damage causes wounds.
Seriously > Wounded.	< Seriously Fatigued.
Moderately > Wounded.	< Moderately Fatigued.
Lightly > Wounded.	< Lightly Fatigued.

CONDITION MONITOR

PHYSICAL	MENTAL
Unconscious.> Possibly dead	< Unconscious. Further damage causes wounds.
Seriously > Wounded.	< Seriously Fatigued.
Moderately > Wounded.	< Moderately Fatigued.
Lightly > Wounded.	< Lightly Fatigued.

CONDITION MONITOR

PHYSICAL	MENTAL
Unconscious.> Possibly dead	< Unconscious. Further damage causes wounds.
Seriously > Wounded.	< Seriously Fatigued.
Moderately > Wounded.	< Moderately Fatigued.
Lightly > Wounded.	< Lightly Fatigued.

CONDITION MONITOR

PHYSICAL	MENTAL
Unconscious.> Possibly dead	< Unconscious. Further damage causes wounds.
Seriously > Wounded.	< Seriously Fatigued.
Moderately > Wounded.	< Moderately Fatigued.
Lightly > Wounded.	< Lightly Fatigued.

CONDITION MONITOR

PHYSICAL	MENTAL
Unconscious.> Possibly dead	< Unconscious. Further damage causes wounds.
Seriously > Wounded.	< Seriously Fatigued.
Moderately > Wounded.	< Moderately Fatigued.
Lightly > Wounded.	< Lightly Fatigued.

FLESH FORM SOLDIERS (FORCE 3)

B	Q	S	C	I	W	E	M	R	Armor
6	6	6	—	1	2	(3)A	—	3	None

Attacks: 6M2 Physical
Skills: Unarmed Combat 3
Powers: Enhanced Senses (Smell), Pain Resistance
Weaknesses: None

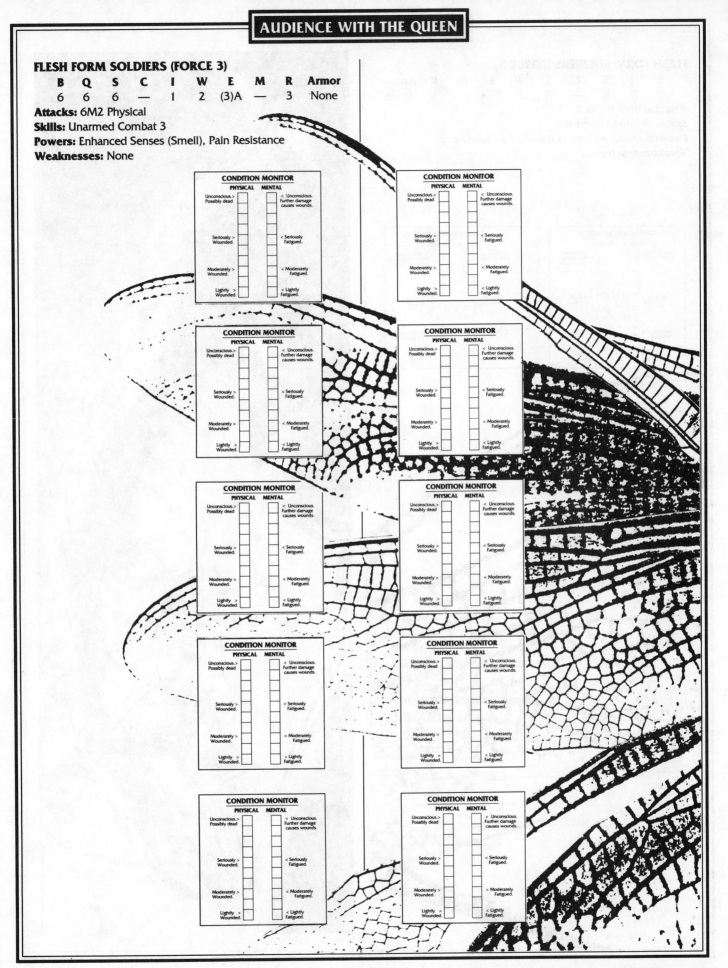

FLESH FORM SOLDIERS (FORCE 5)

B	Q	S	C	I	W	E	M	R	Armor
8	8	8	—	3	2	(5)A	—	5	None

Attacks: 8M2 Physical
Skills: Unarmed Combat 3
Powers: Enhanced Senses (Smell), Pain Resistance
Weaknesses: None

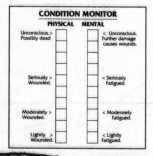
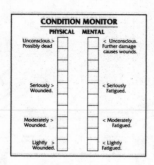

CONDITION MONITOR

PHYSICAL   MENTAL

Unconscious.>
Possibly dead

< Unconscious.
Further damage
causes wounds.

Seriously >
Wounded.

< Seriously
Fatigued.

Moderately >
Wounded.

< Moderately
Fatigued.

Lightly >
Wounded.

< Lightly
Fatigued.

CONDITION MONITOR

PHYSICAL   MENTAL

Unconscious.>
Possibly dead

< Unconscious.
Further damage
causes wounds.

Seriously >
Wounded.

< Seriously
Fatigued.

Moderately >
Wounded.

< Moderately
Fatigued.

Lightly >
Wounded.

< Lightly
Fatigued.

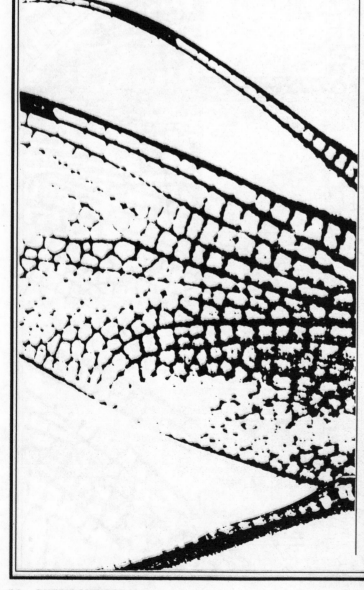

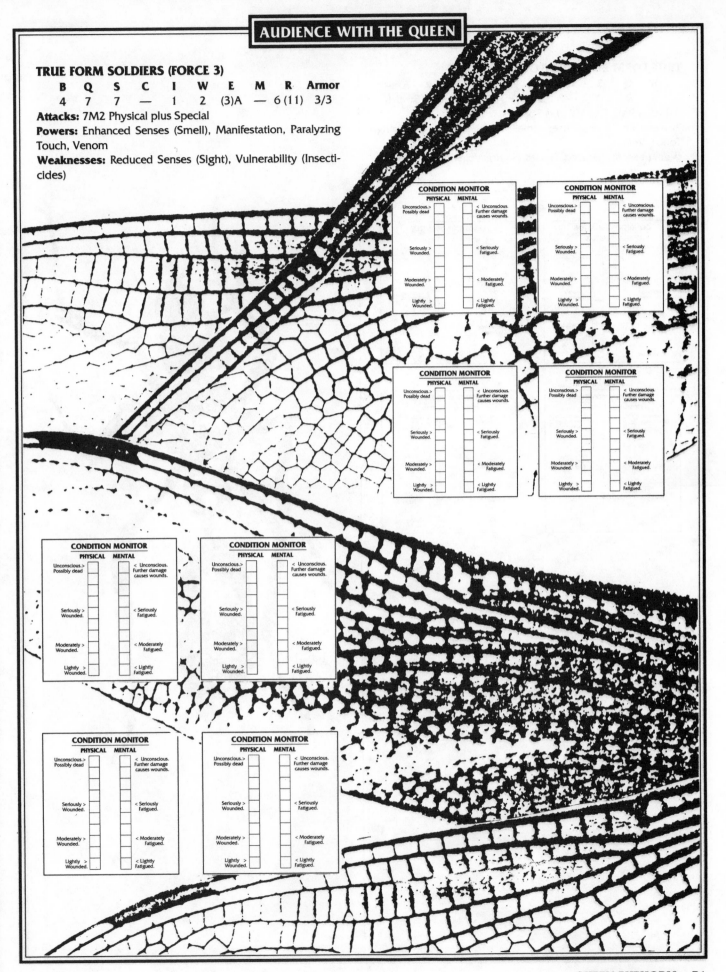

TRUE FORM SOLDIERS (FORCE 3)

B	Q	S	C	I	W	E	M	R	Armor
4	7	7	—	1	2	(3)A	—	6 (11)	3/3

Attacks: 7M2 Physical plus Special
Powers: Enhanced Senses (Smell), Manifestation, Paralyzing Touch, Venom
Weaknesses: Reduced Senses (Sight), Vulnerability (Insecticides)

CONDITION MONITOR

PHYSICAL	MENTAL
Unconscious.> Possibly dead	< Unconscious. Further damage causes wounds.
Seriously > Wounded.	< Seriously Fatigued.
Moderately > Wounded.	< Moderately Fatigued.
Lightly > Wounded.	< Lightly Fatigued.

TRUE FORM SOLDIERS (FORCE 5)

B	Q	S	C	I	W	E	M	R	Armor
6	9	9	—	3	2	(5)A	—	10 (15)	5/5

Attacks: 9M2 Physical plus Special

Powers: Enhanced Senses (Smell), Manifestation, Paralyzing Touch, Venom

Weaknesses: Reduced Senses (Sight), Vulnerability (Insecticides)

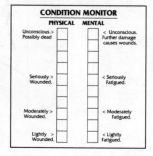

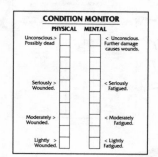

PICKING UP THE PIECES

QUEEN EUPHORIA

When the runners gain control of the Hive Room, they find Euphoria barely visible inside the largest of the cocoons. A close physical examination of the cocoon will reveal that her body is undergoing some kind of change. An astral examination will show an insect-shaped aura dominating her. Any attempt at a Mind Probe of Euphoria will fail. The only result will be the player character getting a severe headache as incomprehensible, alien thoughts flood his mind.

During her time in the cocoon, the Ant Queen is susceptible to Astral Combat. Though astrally present as a Dual Being, she is unable to defend herself. Her Force is 5.

If the runners open the cocoon without banishing or destroying the Queen, Euphoria's body will die and the Queen will be sent screaming back to the alien plane of her origin. If they do manage to banish or destroy the Queen Spirit and then open the cocoon, Euphoria's body will survive, but her mind will be long gone. Her body will also show the beginnings of transformation to the Queen form and so will be crippled. There is no way to "save" Euphoria. She is beyond rescue.

The above paragraph also holds true for any other cocoon scattered about the room that the runners inspect. If left alone, the Queen will emerge fully in just under five weeks, with the other cocoons releasing their occupants in anything from one week to five, depending on the Force of the possessing Spirit.

If the runners leave the cocoons, either MegaMedia or Strice Foods will first analyze them carefully for their potential economic value, then destroy them.

OUTSIDE THE HIVE

When the runners leave the production facility, they meet quite a sight outside. Shortly after they went in, MegaMedia had nearly a full company of Knight Errant troopers move into position around the building. Fearing that the runners might encounter something too powerful for them, Carrone brought in the troops as back-up. If the runners really botch things, the gamemaster can have the Knight Errant units move in and clean up.

Two other matters will also involve the Knight Errant forces. The first is enforcement of the runners' contractual obligation to return the equipment loaned to them for the run. Even with all the firepower the players' team has, the presence of the combat-trained Knight Errant troopers should give them pause.

The second is an option the gamemaster may wish to exploit for a future adventure. Having heard about MegaMedia's request for such a large unit, a Knight Errant executive decided to go along as an observer. He remains in the command vehicle with Carrone, watching as the mayhem breaks out. Should the runners get bogged down during the raid, the gamemaster could have this executive come onto the radio link to give tactical suggestions. At the end of the run, he will commend the runners for their work and offer each 1,000 nuyen for a full report on what they saw, heard, and experienced in the Hive.

PAYMENT

Surprise! Carrone will pay the runners the agreed-upon amount, assuming of course, that all aspects of the contract have been fulfilled. Carrone will stress that the contract forbids them from divulging anything about the run without Carrone's express permission. If pressed, he will waive the clause for Knight Errant.

HEY, CHUMMER, AIN'T THAT US?

Six weeks after the battle in the Hive, MegaMedia will release *Against The Hive Masters,* the fateful sim of the now-retired Euphoria.

Should the runners complain to MegaMedia, the corp will politely remind them that the contract they signed gave the corporation rights to all reproductions or fictionalization of the events of the run.

AWARDING KARMA

This could be a lucrative adventure for the runners. If they survive, they should do well in the Karma department, too.

The team receives the following Karma Points for the run:

A Successful First Kidnapping	5
Destroying the Hive	5
Destroying Queen Euphoria	3

The gamemaster should also award points to individuals using the guidelines on page 160 of the **SR** rules.

INSECT SPIRITS

Two types of Spirits appear in this adventure, Soldier Ant Spirits and Worker Ant Spirits. Though technically present, the Queen Spirit does not actually appear in the adventure. Ant Spirits may appear in either of two forms, True Form or Flesh Form.

The True Form Ant Spirit is the "natural" form and the closest analogy to the Spirit types previously encountered in **Shadowrun.** It has the power of Manifestation, which gives it the ability to operate fully in Astral Space and to manifest in mundane space as well. In Astral Space, the Ant Spirit's statistics are based on its Force, as for normal Spirits. When it manifests in mundane space, use the number given below.

When in Astral Space, the Ant Spirit receives a +5 Initiative bonus to its Reaction, which is calculated normally. It may attack and defend, but cannot use any of its special powers.

In addition to its special powers, the Ant Spirit, when physically manifest, has the power of Immunity to Normal Weapons against all forms of ranged combat, firearm or otherwise. That is, against firearms and ranged attacks of all types, excluding spells. Ant Spirits have "armor" equal to double their Force.

When an attacker uses a mundane weapon against a manifested Spirit in Melee Combat, use Willpower instead of the usual attack skill. Against Spirit foes, unshakeable strength of will is more important than weapon skill. Magical Attacks and attacks using a Spirit's Vulnerability are not subject to this rule.

In appearance, a True Form Ant Spirit is a roughly man-sized ant-form, pristine and unblemished.

Flesh Form Ant Spirits are Spirits in possession of a Human body. They are permanently connected to that body unless forcibly removed through the death of the body, banishment, or destruction in Astral Combat. The physical form of a Flesh Form Ant Spirit is a gruesome cross between a human being and the closest a flesh-and-bone body can get to becoming a giant ant. Each Flesh Form is different, especially among Flesh Form Soldiers.

When possessing a Human or Metahuman body, the Ant Spirit will modify the attributes of the host body. A Worker Spirit will reduce the Host's Physical Attributes by 1 point, while its Mental Attributes change to reflect those of the Spirit listed for the True Form. A Soldier Ant Spirit adds its Force to the Host's Physical Attributes, while the Mental Attributes reflect those listed for the Soldier Spirit's True Form.

The Flesh Form Ant Spirit is a Dual Being, and it may not Astrally Project.

When first summoned, all Ant Spirits must go through an incubatory period while their essence connects with the energies of the astral plane and the mundane world. Usually, the link

to the physical world becomes so strong that the Spirit is unable to detach from the host it used during the incubation period. This is how a Flesh Form Ant Spirit is "born." A True Form Ant Spirit is one who was able to maintain the proper balance between the astral and the physical.

It is possible to defeat an Ant Spirit by destroying its physical body, banishing it, or defeating it in Astral Combat.

The Soldier Spirit is aggressive and combative, fearless and terrifying. The Worker Spirit, on the other hand, is cowardly and ineffective in combat. When attacked, it will emit a piercing screech intended to warn the Hive that danger is near. If, however, any of the cocoons of the Hive are attacked or the Queen is in danger, the Workers will throw themselves in the path of the attack, sacrificing their existence for the greater good.

The Ant Hive

CONDITION MONITOR

PHYSICAL	MENTAL
Unconscious.> Possibly dead	< Unconscious. Further damage causes wounds.
Seriously > Wounded.	< Seriously Fatigued.
Moderately > Wounded.	< Moderately Fatigued.
Lightly > Wounded.	< Lightly Fatigued.

CONDITION MONITOR

PHYSICAL	MENTAL
Unconscious.> Possibly dead	< Unconscious. Further damage causes wounds.
Seriously > Wounded.	< Seriously Fatigued.
Moderately > Wounded.	< Moderately Fatigued.
Lightly > Wounded.	< Lightly Fatigued.

CONDITION MONITOR

PHYSICAL	MENTAL
Unconscious.> Possibly dead	< Unconscious. Further damage causes wounds.
Seriously > Wounded.	< Seriously Fatigued.
Moderately > Wounded.	< Moderately Fatigued.
Lightly > Wounded.	< Lightly Fatigued.

CONDITION MONITOR

PHYSICAL	MENTAL
Unconscious.> Possibly dead	< Unconscious. Further damage causes wounds.
Seriously > Wounded.	< Seriously Fatigued.
Moderately > Wounded.	< Moderately Fatigued.
Lightly > Wounded.	< Lightly Fatigued.

CONDITION MONITOR

PHYSICAL	MENTAL
Unconscious.> Possibly dead	< Unconscious. Further damage causes wounds.
Seriously > Wounded.	< Seriously Fatigued.
Moderately > Wounded.	< Moderately Fatigued.
Lightly > Wounded.	< Lightly Fatigued.

CONDITION MONITOR

PHYSICAL	MENTAL
Unconscious.> Possibly dead	< Unconscious. Further damage causes wounds.
Seriously > Wounded.	< Seriously Fatigued.
Moderately > Wounded.	< Moderately Fatigued.
Lightly > Wounded.	< Lightly Fatigued.

CONDITION MONITOR

PHYSICAL	MENTAL
Unconscious.> Possibly dead	< Unconscious. Further damage causes wounds.
Seriously > Wounded.	< Seriously Fatigued.
Moderately > Wounded.	< Moderately Fatigued.
Lightly > Wounded.	< Lightly Fatigued.

CONDITION MONITOR

PHYSICAL	MENTAL
Unconscious.> Possibly dead	< Unconscious. Further damage causes wounds.
Seriously > Wounded.	< Seriously Fatigued.
Moderately > Wounded.	< Moderately Fatigued.
Lightly > Wounded.	< Lightly Fatigued.

CONDITION MONITOR

PHYSICAL	MENTAL
Unconscious.> Possibly dead	< Unconscious. Further damage causes wounds.
Seriously > Wounded.	< Seriously Fatigued.
Moderately > Wounded.	< Moderately Fatigued.
Lightly > Wounded.	< Lightly Fatigued.

CONDITION MONITOR

PHYSICAL	MENTAL
Unconscious.> Possibly dead	< Unconscious. Further damage causes wounds.
Seriously > Wounded.	< Seriously Fatigued.
Moderately > Wounded.	< Moderately Fatigued.
Lightly > Wounded.	< Lightly Fatigued.

CONDITION MONITOR

PHYSICAL	MENTAL
Unconscious.> Possibly dead	< Unconscious. Further damage causes wounds.
Seriously > Wounded.	< Seriously Fatigued.
Moderately > Wounded.	< Moderately Fatigued.
Lightly > Wounded.	< Lightly Fatigued.

CONDITION MONITOR

PHYSICAL	MENTAL
Unconscious.> Possibly dead	< Unconscious. Further damage causes wounds.
Seriously > Wounded.	< Seriously Fatigued.
Moderately > Wounded.	< Moderately Fatigued.
Lightly > Wounded.	< Lightly Fatigued.

CONDITION MONITOR

PHYSICAL	MENTAL
Unconscious.> Possibly dead	< Unconscious. Further damage causes wounds.
Seriously > Wounded.	< Seriously Fatigued.
Moderately > Wounded.	< Moderately Fatigued.
Lightly > Wounded.	< Lightly Fatigued.

CONDITION MONITOR

PHYSICAL	MENTAL
Unconscious.> Possibly dead	< Unconscious. Further damage causes wounds.
Seriously > Wounded.	< Seriously Fatigued.
Moderately > Wounded.	< Moderately Fatigued.
Lightly > Wounded.	< Lightly Fatigued.

CONDITION MONITOR

PHYSICAL	MENTAL
Unconscious.> Possibly dead	< Unconscious. Further damage causes wounds.
Seriously > Wounded.	< Seriously Fatigued.
Moderately > Wounded.	< Moderately Fatigued.
Lightly > Wounded.	< Lightly Fatigued.

CONDITION MONITOR

PHYSICAL	MENTAL
Unconscious.> Possibly dead	< Unconscious. Further damage causes wounds.
Seriously > Wounded.	< Seriously Fatigued.
Moderately > Wounded.	< Moderately Fatigued.
Lightly > Wounded.	< Lightly Fatigued.

CONDITION MONITOR

PHYSICAL	MENTAL
Unconscious.> Possibly dead	< Unconscious. Further damage causes wounds.
Seriously > Wounded.	< Seriously Fatigued.
Moderately > Wounded.	< Moderately Fatigued.
Lightly > Wounded.	< Lightly Fatigued.

CONDITION MONITOR

PHYSICAL	MENTAL
Unconscious.> Possibly dead	< Unconscious. Further damage causes wounds.
Seriously > Wounded.	< Seriously Fatigued.
Moderately > Wounded.	< Moderately Fatigued.
Lightly > Wounded.	< Lightly Fatigued.

CONDITION MONITOR

PHYSICAL	MENTAL
Unconscious.> Possibly dead	< Unconscious. Further damage causes wounds.
Seriously > Wounded.	< Seriously Fatigued.
Moderately > Wounded.	< Moderately Fatigued.
Lightly > Wounded.	< Lightly Fatigued.

CONDITION MONITOR

PHYSICAL	MENTAL
Unconscious.> Possibly dead	< Unconscious. Further damage causes wounds.
Seriously > Wounded.	< Seriously Fatigued.
Moderately > Wounded.	< Moderately Fatigued.
Lightly > Wounded.	< Lightly Fatigued.

To successfully complete their mission, the player characters are going to have to use their contacts and connections to dig up information on their employers as well as their opposition. Whenever the runners ask to use their sources, see the appropriate section below to decide what information is available to the team.

All attempts to gather information require a test of the characters' Etiquette, Interrogation, or Negotiation Skills. Choose the skill appropriate to the contact being questioned. All tests are done at Target Number 4, unless otherwise indicated. The number of successes determines how much information under each heading that the player character obtains.

The gamemaster roleplays the information-gathering parts of the adventure. If a runner approaches contacts not appropriate to the topic, that character will meet only blank stares. It is risky for a contact to answer questions about highly confidential matters such as corporate security, and perhaps only nuyen or a few extra slaps to the head can make him cough up the information. Bribes are usually in order when the runner rolls three or more successes and gets to the nitty-gritty information. Bribes should range from about 1,000 nuyen for a City Official to a bowl of nutrisoy for a Squatter.

VINCENT BURROUGHS

Burroughs is the Strice Foods executive in charge of Amber Gel. Before Amber Gel became a success, he was unknown in the business world.

Appropriate Contacts: City Official, Company Man, Corporate Official, Corporate Secretary, Former Company Man, Mr. Johnson, Simsense Star, Yakuza Boss, and any Media-related contact.

Available Information:

Burroughs has been receiving a lot of pressure lately for the inexplicable halt in production of Amber Gel. With the Board of Directors of Strice Foods demanding results while Craft demands secrecy, he is caught between a rock and a hard place.

0 Success	No Result
1 – 2 Successes	"Burroughs is a complete incompetent. Perhaps Strice Foods made a good decision when they let him start this Amber Gel project, but promoting him to an executive position was a big mistake. He can't handle the responsibility."
3+ Successes	"Burroughs is a figurehead. The guy really in charge of Amber Gel is some real nutcase. Nobody knows anything about him. The Board of Directors probably don't even know about this guy. That's how good this info is. I think Burroughs took credit for the project, but now Burroughs is getting flak for the mistakes, whether they're his or this other guy's."

ROBERT CARRONE

Carrone is Euphoria's calculating agent and manager, who maneuvered himself into a Vice-Presidency at MegaMedia. Carrone will employ the characters to find Euphoria after Craft and the Hive take her away.

Appropriate Contacts: Club Owner, Detective, Gang Boss or Member, Media Producer, Metahuman Rights Activist, Rocker, Simsense Star, and any Media-related Contact.

Available Information

Information on Carrone is not very pertinent to the adventure, but the players can get an idea of Carrone's devotion to Euphoria from the information their contacts have. The players should also be able to rest easier when they discover that Carrone has a reputation for honest dealing.

0 Success	No Result
1 – 2 Successes	"Carrone's an all-right guy. He gives you a fair shake in a deal. His work is killing him, though. He refuses to give up his other acts even though managing Euphoria takes all his time. His heart is going to stress out unless he slows down or gets a Chiba organ."
3+ Successes	"Carrone's always worried about Euphoria. They say he delayed recording of *Jungle Huntress* because he didn't think there was enough security at their jungle location. Bobby's also worried about that Osprey character who guards Euphoria. I guess the guy's something of a financial leech."

CRAFT/THOMAS DORIN

Dorin is the street shaman who has created the Hive cult in Seattle. When the characters check on the name Craft, they must discover the name of his talismonger shop so that they can continue their search for Euphoria.

Appropriate Contacts: Bartender, Burned-Out Mage, Combat Mage, Decker, Detective, Elven Decker, Fixer, Former Company Man, Former Wage Mage, Gang Boss or Member, Merc, Mr. Johnson, Ork Mercenary, Rigger, Squatter, Street Mage, Street Samurai, Street Shaman, Talismonger, Troll Bouncer, Yakuza Boss.

0 Success	No Result
1 Success	"Craft. That was the name of a runner who worked the shadows about two years ago. He retired and opened up a monger shop. He was a wiz, ya know. The shop was called something like Wiz Crafts or Magic Crafts, something like that."
2 Successes	"Craft's real name is Thomas Dorin. He used to run with a razorguy and another wiz a few years ago. Trouble is, Craft just couldn't help but skim it off the top from his partners or his employer whenever he got the chance. You know the type. Well, he got a bad rep and all his jobs dried up. Then he opened Magic Crafts, a talismonger shop. Last I heard, the place closed up."
3 Successes	"Dorin closed his shop and went way down south into the jungle on some kinda run. I heard he bought the farm on that run."
4+ Successes	"Most people think Craft is dead from that run in South America, but I saw him several weeks ago. He's renovated his shop and he's hanging out there with a bunch of scary-looking dudes."

MAGIC CRAFTS

Though Craft's store has been closed for some time, many people still remember it.
Appropriate Contacts: Street Cop, Any Magical Contact.

0 Success	No Result
1 – 2 Successes	"Magic Crafts? Wasn't that Tom Dorin's place? Use'ta run under the name Craft, I think. Get it? Craft… Magic Crafts? Pretty wiz, eh?"
3+ Successes	"Yeah, sure, Magic Crafts. That's up in Redmond by James Lake, ain't it? Guy named Craft used to run it. Had a real sick fascination for some simsense star, if I remember right."

EUPHORIA

BEFORE HIVE KIDNAPPING

Few people in this town know anything of Euphoria beyond her life as a simsense star. Thomas Carrone does, but he's not talking. There are rumors, of course, but they have no bearing on the adventure. But the player characters don't know that, do they?
Appropriate Contacts: Bartender, Bodyguard, Club Owner, Club Habitué, Corporate Official (Media-related), Fan, Media Producer, Newsman/Media Entrepreneur, Reporter, Rocker, Simsense Star, Any Media Type.

0 Success	The gamemaster should make up some blatantly obvious false rumor. The wilder the better.
1 – 2 Successes	"Jumpers, yes, I've met her. One'a the nicest people, too. Real person, down to earth. One'a us."
3 Successes	"What a bitch! Geez! A year ago, I saw her refuse to sign an autograph for a little kid who was just going nuts 'cause Euphoria was within a meter of him. She just blew him off. She doesn't deserve to be a star."
4+ Successes	"I hear she had a real falling-out with her big co-star, what's his name? Anyway, I hear he's fit to be tied, which I also hear is what he likes best."

SECURITY AROUND EUPHORIA

Appropriate Contacts (Target 6): Bodyguard, Company Man (current or Former), Corporate Official (Media-related), Corporate Secretary (Media-related), Fan, Fixer, Media Producer, Mercenary (any race), Rocker, Simsense Star.
Available Information:

Euphoria has retained Michael Adams, street name Osprey, as her personal bodyguard ever since the early days of her stardom. For extra security, Osprey has brought in his friend Alexander Cross to provide magical support. Additionally, Strice Foods pays for a team of Knight Errant security guards to protect her around the clock.

0 Success	No Result.
1 – 2 Successes	"Well, any time I've seen her in public, she's always protected by some English guy. Pretty lucky assignment, if ya know what I mean."
3 – 4 Successes	"A guy called Osprey has been her regular bodyguard for almost as long as I've heard about her. They usually bring in some extra security when on the road. Freelance stuff."
5+ Successes	"Strice is paying for a team of Knight Errant guards to watch over her. I've also heard that Osprey brought in an old friend of his to help out. Magical kinda guy."

PUBLIC APPEARANCES

Street posters, simsense magazines, regular prints, and broadcast advertisements are currently drilling the public with information on how and where to see Euphoria in her three upcoming appearances. Friday, she's supposed to be at the Renraku Arcology. Saturday, she's appearing at a small coliseum at the south end of the city, and Sunday, she's scheduled for a park near the Aztechnology Pyramid. Euphoria will appear and give a brief speech. It is rumored that she will announce her next sim, *Jungle Huntress*, though many entertainment people already know a lot about it. Along with all of the promotional hoopla for Amber Gel, Strice Foods is promising to give out a never-before-released simsense chip of Euphoria. The chip is a five-minute clip of Euphoria exclaiming about Amber Gel while she enjoys tasting some. All the chips are rigged to burn out after one use, giving the audience one taste through Euphoria's senses and then forcing them to buy Amber Gel if they want more.

Strice Foods will put on their promotional shows, even with Euphoria missing, but the shows will flop. The first show at the Renraku Arcology is a public embarrassment for Strice Foods. The second show at the coliseum ends in rioting. The city government cancels the third show to prevent further riots. See the **Player Handout** for details on the public reaction to Euphoria's first disappearance.

AFTER HIVE KIDNAPPING

Other than the general buzz about Euphoria's first disappearance, there is no information on the street after the second kidnapping. Gossip ranges from speculation that Euphoria vanished to give herself a vacation to rumors that she's run off with the son of a local yakuza oyabun.

OSPREY

Appropriate Contacts: Armorer, Bartender, Bodyguard, Club Owner, Elven Hitman, Media Producer, Merc, Mercenary (Any Race), Rocker, Any Street Type.
Available Information:

Osprey has been guarding Euphoria for a year and a half. For her upcoming appearances in Seattle, he has asked his old running partner Stone to help guard Euphoria. Osprey can be a rough character, but he also likes to play up the English gentleman side of his personality.

0 Success	No Result
1 Successes	"Osprey, you say. Haven't heard that name from a runner in almost two years. He used to run the shadows. Tough as nails, that guy, real mercenary. I remember he had some cyber mods. I think he banked a lot of chips. Last I heard, he was a bodyguard for some big-name star."
2+ Successes	"Osprey was a man who got the job done. Sort of a tough guy but pretty boy. Flaunted his English background like he was some kind of king. He used to run with a bunch of guys. All of them are dead, I think, except one mage named Stone. Last I heard, Osprey had landed a job guarding some simstar. I think it might even be Euphoria."

STONE

Alexander Cross used to run the shadows with Osprey under the street name of Stone. The two have remained casual friends ever since their team broke up.
Appropriate Contacts: Bartender, Combat Mage, Fixer, Mr. Johnson, Talismonger, Any Street Type
Available Information:

Stone now owns a lore shop, but someone else is running it for him ever since Osprey hired him to help guard Euphoria. He is a powerful magician who has the resources to summon Elementals whenever needed.

0 Success	No Result
1 Successes	"Stone's real name is Alexander Cross. He studied magic at UCLA. He must have gotten a doctorate or something 'cause he was good back in the days when he ran the shadows. He retired and started working in a library, if you can believe that."
2 Successes	"Stone was a rich wiz when he was running. He had fetishes and ritual material to burn, so to speak. You could always be sure he had an Elemental or two at his beck and call."
3+ Successes	"I heard recently Stone was taking a few days off and hooking up with some old associates. Maybe he's running again."

LUDIVENKO

Appropriate Contacts: City Official, Company Man, Detective, Former Company Man, Former Wage Mage, Mr. Johnson, Any Corp Type, Any Government Type.

Available Information

The characters may discover that Ludivenko is financing their first run. Most of the current rumors on Ludivenko deal with the corp's reaction to Amber Gel's success. They have hired a team to kidnap Euphoria, and they are also planning to market a new product, Blue Bacosoy, to compete with Amber Gel. They hope to get Euphoria to endorse Blue Bacosoy after her absences discredit Amber Gel.

---

1 Success	"Well, you can be sure Ludivenko is not too happy about the success of this new Amber Gel stuff. Mind you, Seattle's only the testing ground. Amber Gel is bound to cut into Ludivenko's world share of the stuffer market. The Ludivenko people can't find out anything about this Amber Gel. Strice Foods knows how to keep a secret."
2 Successes	"Amber Gel hit Ludivenko the only place corporations get hurt, at the bank. So Ludivenko is bringing out a clone product of Amber Gel, something called Blue Bacosoy. They want to get the jump on Strice Foods in the continental market, but Ludivenko's going to need some big promotions to do it."
3+ Successes	"Ludivenko's new thing, Blue Bacosoy, is going to be endorsed by Euphoria, or so they hope. I heard that Ludivenko was hiring a team to snatch Euphoria away from Strice to either employ her or force her to promote Blue Bacosoy instead of Amber Gel."

STRICE FOODS

Home Office Location: Birmingham, AL, CAS
President/CEO: Deloris Stanton
Principal Divisions
Division Name: Faucet Flavors
  Division Head: Zachary Fynche
  Chief Products/Services: Faucet Flavors produces an extensive line of nutrisoy flavoring agents. It is the largest division of Strice Foods.
Division Name: REAL Foods
  Division Head: Jack Tauber
  Chief Products/Services: This division of Strice Foods produces a full line of organic foods. Their chief products are hydroponically grown vegetables.
Division Name: Modern Masterpieces
  Division Head: Vincent Burroughs
  Chief Products/Services: Production and distribution of mass-market food stuffs (or stuffers) such as Best O'Da Bunch, Crackle Cakes, Zap Softies, and the current runaway sensation, Amber Gel.

Business Profile:

Strice Foods is a minor player in the international food business, but if they can market Amber Gel properly, it could be their first big-ticket item. Give players handout 1.

Security/Military Forces:

Knight Errant Security has a contract with Strice for more important security assignments. The firm also has a small internal security force.

Local Rumors:

All rumors about Strice have to do with Amber Gel. The information is subdivided into General Info and Computer Systems. Consult the appropriate heading to answer the kind of questions the characters are asking.

GENERAL STRICE INFORMATION

Appropriate Contacts: City Official, Company Man, Detective, Former Company Man, Former Wage Mage, Mr. Johnson, Any Corp Type.

0 Success	No Result
1 – 2 Successes	"Strice Foods is in a tough bind. They've got this Vincent Burroughs fellow in charge of their hot new item, Amber Gel. Trouble is, Burroughs isn't doing his job so they need to move him out or demote him, but Burroughs is the only guy there who knows all the secrets of Amber Gel. Burroughs may be messing up Amber Gel, but he was smart enough to make himself invaluable to Strice by not releasing his secrets."
3+ Successes	"Burroughs is telling his bosses that he has no control over increasing production. I think he's doing something illegal that he can't control."

STRICE COMPUTER SYSTEM

Appropriate Contacts: Corporate Decker, Decker, Dwarven Technician, Elven Decker, Fixer, Technician.

0 Success	No Result
1 – 2 Successes	"Yeah, Strice gave Amber Gel its own computer system. It's like they were daring people to hack it, if you ask me. I've got a friend, not as good a friend as you, of course, but this friend took a crack at the system. One of his best homemade utilities got swallowed and poisoned. At that point, he decided to cut his losses and just left the system."
3+ Successes	"I've got the system's SAN address. It'll cost you, of course. Yeah, that's enough, I mean we're friends, so I want to give you a deal, right? The number is 2206-312-1752. Better use it soon, though. I think it changes every week."

STRICE RUMORS

In addition to the above public information, the streets are awash with rumors as well.

Appropriate Contacts

Corporate Official (Media- or Finance-related), Corporate Secretary (Media- or Finance-related), Media Producer, Newsman/Media Entrepreneur, Reporter, Rocker, Simsense Star, Any Media Type.

0 Success	No Result
1 – 2 Successes	"Yeah, I hear the Brighton thing is gonna cost MegaMedia billions. They are not happy people. Don't know what they would do if one of their other stars tried to walk."
3 – 4 Successes	"Now that Brighton's left MegaMedia, the company's become fair game. Every other half-nuyen corp in the biz is probably gonna try to raid them now."
5+ Successes	"Supposedly, Aztechnology is suing the drek out of MegaMedia over the helicopter that crashed near the pyramid the night Brighton got out. Lone Star's been named as co-defendant."

MEGAMEDIA ENTERTAINMENT INC.

[The following is public information, accessible through any public datanet.]

Home Office: Seattle, UCAS
President/CEO: William Welsh
Principal Divisions
    Division Name: MegaMedia Productions
        Division Head: Andrea Stueban
        Chief Products/Services: Simsense and trideo production
    Division Name: MegaMedia International
        Division Head: Nick Nathan
        Chief Products/Services: Simsense and trideo chip and program distribution.

Business Profile:

One of the "Big Six" international simsense/trideo production and distribution corporations, MegaMedia owes much of its success to its uncanny ability to find and groom potential new stars. All their major talents, Cindy Cyclone, Ted Morgan, David and Helen Variable, Honey Brighton, and Euphoria, were all relative unknowns before signing with MegaMedia. The recent defection of Brighton and her famed producer, Witt Lipton, has industry analysts speculating about possible internal problems within this media giant's corporate structure. Another blow like the Brighton defection could be fatal.

Security/Military Forces:

MegaMedia formerly employed Lone Star for all facility and personal security, but have recently terminated in favor of a contract with Knight Errant.

CRAFT

The son of wage slave parents, Thomas Dorin grew up in Seattle, learning to survive on the streets. Thomas learned shamanic magic from an old, crazed Coyote shaman who lived as a squatter. The old man gave him lessons in ritual and spellcasting in exchange for food, and then Dorin would go off to practice what he had learned.

By the time the shaman died, Thomas had learned enough to use his magical talents as a shadowrunner. His running partners gave him the streetname of Craft because of his cunning solutions to problems that arose during runs. Craft had built a small reputation before he blew his career by repeatedly double-crossing his employers and his chummers. Word spread through the corporate community, and Craft was soon black-listed from runs.

Craft dropped his streetname, and used the small fortune he had accumulated to open a talismonger shop. He called the shop Magic Crafts and built a large clientele. The life of a merchant was starting to bore Dorin about the time that his Fixer, Solomon Daniels, offered him a run. Dorin jumped at the chance to relive his old lifestyle of danger and trickery.

In **Queen Euphoria**, Craft appears as a filthy, unkempt man. His long, blond hair is tangled and dirty, and his clothes are covered with brown stains from regurgitation.

Craft's personality shows wide swings in behavior. As a Coyote shaman, he is a trickster and sometimes a traitor to his friends or employer. As a businessman, Craft is respectable and friendly. While under the influence of the Ant totem, Craft is crazed with power.

His fascination, or rather psychotic fixation, with Euphoria is the cause of most of his troubles. That and his desire for personal power led to his separation from Coyote and his acceptance of the Ant totem.

Attributes
- Body: 4
- Quickness: 3
- Strength: 3
- Charisma: 5
- Intelligence: 5
- Willpower: 6
- Essence: 6
- Magic: 6
- Reaction: 4

Dice Pools
- Astral: 15
- Defense (Armed): 1
- Defense (Unarmed): 3
- Dodge: 3
- Magic: 6

Skills
- Conjuring: 5
- Etiquette (Corporate): 1
- Etiquette (Street): 4
- Firearms (Pistols): 4
- Magic Theory: 6
- Negotiation: 4
- Sorcery (Spellcasting): 6
- Stealth (Urban): 4
- Unarmed Combat: 3

Special Skills:
- Evaluate Magical Goods: 5
- Metalworking: 3
- Woodworking: 3

Gear
- Ares Predator [10 (clip), 2 extra clips, 4M2]
- Real Leather Clothing (0/2)
- Sleep Spell Focus (2)

Spells
- **Combat:**
  - Mana Bolt: 5
  - Sleep: 5
- **Detection:**
  - Clairvoyance: 4
- **Illusion:**
  - Confusion: 5
  - Mask: 6
  - Stimulation: 4
- **Manipulation:**
  - Armor: 6
  - Levitate Person: 4

Totem
- Ant (no special benefits)

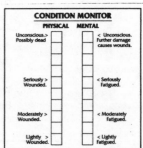

CONDITION MONITOR

	PHYSICAL	MENTAL	
Unconscious.>Possibly dead			< Unconscious.Further damage causes wounds.
Seriously >Wounded.			< SeriouslyFatigued.
Moderately >Wounded.			< ModeratelyFatigued.
Lightly >Wounded.			< LightlyFatigued.

EUPHORIA

Amanda Lockhart is the daughter of two trideo stars. Her parents were actors when broadcasting was still television, and they continued with the advent of trideo. Coming from such a background, it was only natural for Amanda to follow her family's path. Encouraged by her parents, she became a child trideo actor. When simsense became popular, her parents were quick to push her in that direction, firmly believing in the future of entertainment technology.

Amanda's first jobs were as extras in simsense production. Her big break came when she changed from her parents' agent to her current agent, Robert Carrone, who specialized in sim-stars. With the stage name of Euphoria, Amanda made a series of low-budget sims with rather erotic themes. The sims estranged her parents, but catapulted her to stardom. Since then, Euphoria has made six full-budget sims, teaming up with male star Hans Vandenburg on four of them. Her next sim, *Jungle Huntress,* will soon go into production on location in the Aztlan jungles.

Euphoria is blessed with beauty. She is dazzling without surgery or even make-up. She prefers her hair light brown, though it's been any number of colors during her career. Her eyes are brown and still the original organic models.

Though she is twenty-one years old, Euphoria is still a little girl. She is very arrogant, having been spoiled by the benefits of her position. Her circle of close associates are used to her, but those beyond the inner circle have difficulty getting along with her.

Euphoria is something of a recluse. She has not learned how to cope with fans who idolize her and yet sometimes want to tear her to pieces.

Attributes
- Body: 2
- Quickness: 4
- Strength: 2
- Charisma: 6
- Intelligence: 4
- Willpower: 2
- Essence: 5
- Reaction: 4

Skills
- Electronics (Simsense Equipment): 3
- Etiquette (Corporate): 2
- Etiquette (Media): 3
- Etiquette (Street): 1
- Negotiation: 2

Special Skills
- Acting: 5
- Dance: 2
- Simsense Acting: 6

Dice Pools
- Defense (Armed): 1
- Defense (Unarmed): 1
- Dodge: 4

Cyberware
- Datajack
- Sense Link (w/internal transmitter)

Gear

Everything found in her condo. In public, she wears a Long Coat (4/2).

CONDITION MONITOR		
PHYSICAL		**MENTAL**
Unconscious.> Possibly dead		< Unconscious. Further damage causes wounds.
Seriously > Wounded.		< Seriously Fatigued.
Moderately > Wounded.		< Moderately Fatigued.
Lightly > Wounded.		< Lightly Fatigued.

ROBERT CARRONE

Robert Carrone is a born and bred corp man. He began his career at nine years old as a go-fer for a video director. He learned the biz quickly and was in the right place at the right time to turn Amanda Lockhart into Euphoria. When MegaMedia acquired Euphoria's contract a few years back, Carrone was set for life.

Carrone is calm and collected. He has worked hard all his life to achieve his current position and he intends to keep it. He uses every ruthless trick in the corporate world to hang onto what is his.

He is fairly loyal to MegaMedia, having worked for the corp all his life. But he's never been offered a better deal elsewhere.

Attributes
Body: 3
Quickness: 4
Strength: 2
Charisma: 3
Intelligence: 4
Willpower: 3
Essence: 5.4
Reaction: 4

Skills
Etiquette (Corporate): 6
Etiquette (Media): 5
Firearms: 3
Negotiation: 5

Dice Pools
Defense (Armed): **1**
Defense (Unarmed): 1
Dodge: 4

Cyberware
Datajack
Display Link
Headware Memory 30 Mp

Gear
Armor Clothing
Ceska vz/120 [18 (clip), 3M2]
Pocket Secretary
Wristphone with vidscreen

CONDITION MONITOR

PHYSICAL	MENTAL
Unconscious.> Possibly dead	< Unconscious. Further damage causes wounds.
Seriously > Wounded.	< Seriously Fatigued.
Moderately > Wounded.	< Moderately Fatigued.
Lightly > Wounded.	< Lightly Fatigued.

MEGAMEDIA INCORPORATED

CONTRACT

This Agreement, in consideration of the mutual covenants of the parties heretofore mentioned, is made at _____, this ____day of_____ 2050 by and between **MEGAMEDIA INCORPORATED**, Seattle UCAS, a Multinational Corporation, (herein called **"MEGAMEDIA CORPORATION"**), and

(herein "Contractee").

THE CONTRACTEE

1. Hereby warrants that he shall make all due and proper effort to undertake the operation for **MEGAMEDIA INCORPORATED** as described below—

(Attach sufficient Riders as neccessary)

(herein called "Mission")
and that he will attempt to accomplish said mission using all resources at his disposal in a proper and efficient manner. Said resources, provided by **MEGAMEDIA INCORPORATED**, as stated below, if consisting of physical weaponry, electronic gear, or vehicles will be returned to **MEGAMEDIA INCORPORATED** at the conclusionn of said Mission, minus expendables.

2. States that he shall be exclusively responsible for return of said resources and will be, and is, solely responsible for recompensation of **MEGAMEDIA INCORPORATED** for non-expendable resources lost during the course of the Mission.

3. Agrees to discuss no item, fact, piece of information, or data relating to said Mission to anyone inside or outside of **MEGAMEDIA INCOPORATED** without the expressed written consent of a senior official of **MEGAMEDIA INCORPORATED** from the public relations department, or an executive of the firm.

4. Hereby assigns and transfers to **MEGAMEDIA INCORPORATED** and its assigns the following rights:

a. All rights in the work of dramatization, motion picture, trideo, simulated senses, television rights (including rights of mechanical recording, transmission and reproduction by radio, television and any other medium known or to be known), in the United Canadian and American States, and in its possessions, and in all foreign countries.

b. The full and exclusive right to publish, print, reprint, copy, sell, vend and market the work and any subsequent or revised editions thereof (including regular trade and "paperback" editions), during the whole term of its copyright and all the renewals thereof in the United Canadian and American States and its possessions, and throughout the world.

c. Second and third serial rights, abridgement, condensation, selection, and other serial and publication rights following book publication, of, in, or to said work in the United Canadian and American States. This includes the rights to issue or license to issue said work in a Book Club edition.

d. The sole and exclusive right to grant licenses for the publication of said work or parts thereof in the English language, or for translations of said work into foreign languages, and for the exercise of the other rights enumerated in paragraphs a, b, c above, in any foreign country.

5. Agrees to accomplish said Mission at indicated time, within the means at his disposal, in exchange for the terms of payment indicated below.

6 The Contractee agrees not to undertake a Mission against **MEGAGMEDIA CORPORATION** in any way connected to the facts or circumstances of this contracted Mission, in perpetuity, and agrees not to undertake any Mission of any kind against **MEGAMEDIA CORPORATION** for thirty (30) days following the completion of this contracted Mission.

MEGAMEDIA CORPORATION AGREES:

5. To support the Contractee to the best of their ability in the execution of the contracted Mission within the time frame specified in separate negotiations.

6. To provide the Contractee with all available information and intelligence regarding said contract Mission and its inclusive elements.

7. To assume full responsibility for said Mission within the agreements and provisions of the Corporate Interaction Act of 2038 as agreed to and signed by **MEGAMEDIA CORPORATION,** and filed with the Center For Corporate Actions, Paris, France, on the date of inception.

8 To pay to the Contractee less any sum of money which **MEGAMEDIA CORPORATION** may be required to deduct or withhold by reason of non-compliance with the letter or spirit of aforementioned contract points, the following sums on the following schedule:

This agreement shall be binding upon and inure to the benefit of the executors, administrators and assigns of the Contractees and upon the successors and assigns of **MEGAMEDIA CORPORATION**.

IN WITNESS WHEREOF, the parties have executed this agreement and affixed their signatures hereto on the date first above mentioned.

CONTRACTEE   MEGAMEDIA CORPORATION,
                                              by

_____   _____
                                       Robert Carrone, Vice President

As Overseen By, in accordance with Intermediary Law,

_____
August Dorn, Independent Contract Overseer

TODAY'S HEADLINES:

INTERNATIONAL
•A European policlub known as "the Revenants" takes credit for the recent bombing of corporate shuttle.
•A demonstration by Australian government employees demanding higher pay increases is forcibly broken up with the aid of several corporate security teams.

LOCAL
•City officials warn that travel into all tribal lands may be further restricted.
•Lone Star confiscates over 20,000 BTL chips in breaking up one of the city's largest smuggling rings.
•Universal Brotherhood announces plans for three more Barrens missions.

BUSINESS
•Lone Star's city contract is up for renewal. Negotiations begin next week.
•Strice Foods announces it is withdrawing its new product, Amber Gel, from the market.

ENTERTAINMENT
•MegaMedia announces the retirement of their mega-big simstar, Euphoria.

SPORTS
•"Mauler" Tate, star of the Screamers, is given his unconditional release for refusal to take experimental steroids.

REVENANTS CLAIM BOMB

LONDON (BNI)— The elusive European policlub known as "the Revenants" today claimed responsibility for last weeks's bombing of the Werner-Voss corporate shuttle on its run from Berlin to London. The shuttle, a British National Aerospace T306, exploded over the English Channel, killing all 175 aboard. From examined wreckage, aviation experts have determined the cause to be an incendiary device. How the device was planted in spite of stringent security measures remains a mystery.

It has been reported that BBC-VI received an extensive data-pak from the Revenants detailing the nature and placement of the explosive device. Authorities have yet to release any information, pending further investigation.
Continued on page I2.

STRICE DROPS AMBER GEL

SEATTLE (API)— In a surprise move, Strice Foods today announced that it was suspending distribution of its popular stuffer, Amber Gel. Strice representatives denied reports that this was in any way connected to the cancelled Euphoria promotions just over a week ago.

Strice represenatives also denied published reports that MegaMedia, the simsense giant, had launched a military operation against Strice's Amber Gel production facility last month. MegaMedia had no comment.

Industry experts reacted with amazement at the Strice announcement. "That's wild," said Nik Elliot, industry analyst. "Amber Gel is their numero uno. Why on earth would they kill it?"
Continued on page B1

EUPHORIA RETIRES, FANS WAIL

SEATTLE (EntNet)—MegaMedia Inc., the simsense conglomerate, announced yesterday that their highest-grossing star, Euphoria, would be retiring following the completion of her latest sim. MegaMedia spokesperson Angela Lane, citing "personal confidentiality," refused comment on whether or not the star's retirement was linked to her recent abduction. Knight Errant Security is conducting an investigation into the abduction along with local Lone Star forces, but it has not yet issued a statement. Rumors continue to circulate as to the nature of that abduction, some saying it was a failed kidnapping by a deranged fan.

According to Lane, Euphoria would not be making a public statement until after the completion of *Against the Hive Masters* (formerly *Jungle Princess*), her latest project currently in studio production at MegaMedia. Euphoria's longtime manager, Robert Carrone, has said that *Hive Masters* is already over-budget and is still not close to completion.

Lou Buckminster, founder amd president of the international Euphoria fanclub, Euphoriacs, expressed shock and disbelief. "It can't really be true! She wouldn't do that to us! She wouldn't leave us like this. We're her fans, we made her famous! She owes us!" Mr. Buckminster went on to encourage all of Euphoria's fans worldwide to fax the star and convince her to reconsider her retirement.

Euphoria burst upon the simsense scene in 2048 with *Shotgun Blues,* a bizarre tale of a crazed Indian who kidnapped a native tourist and dragged her through the Native American Nations while he searched for his long-lost shotgun.

Industry insiders continue to speculate that Euphoria's retirement stems from personal conflict with her frequent co-star, Hans Vandenburg. MegaMedia publicists, however, deny such rumors. Said Carrone, "Sure she bugs him occasionally, but she does that to everyone."

PLAYER HANDOUT 1

Excerpt from the Business Section of the Seattle Speedprint

Strice Foods Inc. has chosen Seattle as its test marketing area for a new stuffer named Amber Gel. The new product is hitting the glutted stuffer market with a bang and promises to become one of Strice Foods' biggest sellers. Some mystery surrounds the product, however, both in its top-secret production and in the bizarre strategies used to market it.

Strice Foods, well known for their Faucet Flavors line of soy-flavoring agents, has held only a small share of the large stuffer market. Top executives apparently want to turn that around with the company's new product, Amber Gel. After a month of testing in the Seattle area, the product has met with enormous success. It appears that Strice Foods cannot keep up with demand for the product in the rapidly growing Seattle market.

Vincent Burroughs, the Strice executive responsible for the success of Amber Gel, is one of the few Strice Foods personnel who is privy to the secrets of Amber Gel. It is not new for a stuffer manufacturer to conceal the ingredients and production techniques of its stuffers, but secrecy measures have never been taken to the extremes seen in the case of Amber Gel. It is not only the product's ingredients and production methods that are secret but even the location of the production site is a mystery. It is rumored that even members of Strice Foods' Board of Directors remain ignorant of the product's secrets.

More alarming than its secrecy are the strange marketing strategies employed by Burroughs and his team. They have managed to book the simsense star Euphoria for three public appearances in Seattle to support Amber Gel. These appearances come on top of a demand that already exceeds the current supply of their product. As Euphoria has never before made a public personal appearance, these promotions must certainly have cost Strice Foods a bundle of nuyen. Nuyen better spent increasing their production in the Seattle area.

It is also a mystery why Strice Foods hasn't gone ahead with regional or continental production and distribution of a product that is such an obvious success. Perhaps Strice Foods was correct in choosing Burroughs to start the product off, but now Amber Gel's success may have gone beyond Burroughs' business and managerial skills.

The confusion surrounding the product makes Strice Foods a risky investment, the potential for either profit or loss are about equal at the moment. If Strice Foods and Vincent Burroughs can get full-scale production started, they'll capture a huge market share. Too much delay, however, and rival stuffer producers will surely bring out clone products to beat Amber Gel to the market niche. You can be sure that Amber Gel's success has not gone unnoticed in the boardrooms of Strice Foods competitors.

PLAYER HANDOUT 2

Excerpt from the Metro Section of the Seattle Speedprint

Amanda Lockhart, otherwise known as the simsense star Euphoria, disappeared from her penthouse home Thursday night. Her disappearance came shortly before Euphoria was scheduled to make several weekend appearances in the Seattle area. Lone Star spokesmen say that an investigation is underway. The only officially released information is that the star was definitely kidnapped, but no suspects were mentioned.

Vincent Burroughs, Strice Foods spokesman, blames rival corporations for the star's disappearance. Euphoria's scheduled weekend appearances were to be promotions for Strice Foods' new Amber Gel product. In an interview, Burroughs stated that rival companies "were jealous of the success of our new product. They had to prevent Euphoria's promotions, and [kidnapping Euphoria] is the kind of underhanded techniques you can expect from our competitors." Lone Star would not confirm or deny the possibility that a corporate extraction team was responsible for the kidnapping. One Lone Star source did admit that evidence on the scene suggests that the kidnapping did not appear to have been a professional job. He cited that "the type of weapons apparently used and the sloppiness of execution suggests the likelihood that a fan cult gang was responsible rather than a team of professionals."

Though Euphoria was absent, the first scheduled promotional event at the Renraku Arcology was not cancelled Friday afternoon. Attendance was meager and the crowd restless and angry. Strice Foods announced that it was not planning to cancel either of the succeeding two promotional events, either. One city government spokesman announced that it might have to cancel the shows to prevent riots from breaking out among the crowds when Euphoria did not appear.

DMZ

DOWNTOWN MILITARIZED ZONE

A BOXED GAME FOR SHADOWRUN

PARANORMAL
ANIMALS
OF NORTH AMERICA
A SHADOWRUN SOURCEBOOK

NELSON

GARGOYLE